DESIGN & TECHNOLOGY

Techniques and Resources

Colin Chapman

Advisory Teacher for Design & Technology

Val Charles

Advisory Teacher for Business Education

Mike Finney

Head of Technology,
William Farr C of E Comprehensive School, Welton

Michael Horsley

Advisory Teacher for Information Technology

Heather Jeffrey

Head of Home Economics,
King Edward VI School, Louth

Malcolm Moyes

Information Technology Coordinator,
Boston High School for Girls

CollinsEducational

An imprint of HarperCollinsPublishers

Published in 1993 by CollinsEducational
An imprint of HarperCollins*Publishers*
77-85 Fulham Palace Road
Hammersmith
London W6 8JB

ISBN 0 00 322062 1

Designed by Ken Vail Graphic Design,
(Production management Glennis Starling)

Cover design by Raynor Design
Cover photograph by Chris Gilbert

Illustrated by Mike Badrocke, Ann Baum, Katy Bradbury,
Tim Cooke, Dalton/Jacobs Illustration, David Lock,
Malcolm Ryan
School location photographs by Peter Sharp, Studio 7; and
Nicola Cornish
Picture research by Caroline Mitchell

Printed by Cambus Litho Ltd., East Kilbride

Commissioning Editor: Graham Bradbury
Project Editor: Philippa Moyle
Editor: Katherine King
Production: Ken Ruskin

CONTENTS

WHAT'S THIS BOOK ABOUT?

This book is called *Design & Technology: Techniques and Resources*. It contains hints and tips to help you to make things, and useful information to help you to understand more about Design & Technology.

Making things in Design & Technology will involve you in using many different materials. These materials include food, textiles, clay, wood, metal, plastic, paper and card. In fact, there is no limit to the range of materials that your research may lead you to consider.

Using different materials usually means using different tools to suit the materials. The tools you will use range from pens and pencils to machines, such as cookers and word processors. Whatever tools you are working with, this book can help you to use them correctly and safely.

This is also a resource book, so you can use it like a reference book to look up information. It contains chapters on business and economics, energy, and electrical, mechanical and structural systems. These are all part of Design & Technology.

In D&T, you will learn to:
Some pages have boxes (like this one) in which you can find out what you will be learning about.

EXTRAS

Extras are challenges to encourage you to find out more about Design & Technology. Try this Extra now. Look at the things around you. How many different materials do you think were used to make them? Make a list of some of the materials.

1 TEXTILES

People have relied on textiles for clothing and shelter throughout the ages. In the Stone Age, people wore animal skins to keep them warm, and their homes had woven reeds on the floor and animal skins at the doorway. Over the centuries, new technologies have brought greater wealth and an ever-increasing range of fabrics, many of them synthetic (artificial). Different cultures have developed their own styles of dress and designs for home furnishings. The basic need for clothing and shelter still needs to be met, just as in the Stone Age, but today it is met in thousands of different ways.

Clothing

Clothing can tell you a lot about the person wearing it. You may be able to guess what job they do, what their religion is, what school they belong to, or even their particular interests or hobbies. Fig. 1.1 shows the State Opening of Parliament. The 'Beefeaters' can be identified by their bright red outfits and black hats. Can you identify anyone else by their clothing?

Fig. 1.1

In D&T, you will learn to:

recognise the historical and cultural background to design and technological developments

The illustration shows a selection of clothes that identify a person's job, religion or situation. In a small group, write down a list of any other clothes that identify a person. When you have finished, a spokesperson from each group can read out the group's list. Between all the groups there should be an enormous variety of outfits.

6

Fig. 1.3

Textiles inside and outside the home

In a similar way to clothing, home furnishings can tell you a lot about people's taste and, sometimes, their wealth or status. Household textiles have many different functions. Why do you have carpets, curtains, towels, bed linen and upholstered furniture? What part do textiles play in making your life comfortable?

Textiles also play a large part in the world outside the home. How many outdoor uses of textiles can you think of? For instance, if you go camping you will need a tent. The fabric that a tent is made from is very different from the kind of fabric used inside the home.

Raw materials

In your study of textiles, you will discover the enormous variety of raw materials that are used to make textiles. These raw materials have a wide range of **properties**. This means that some raw materials are very strong, some are water-resistant, and others keep the warmth in. The illustration shows textiles with different functions to perform. The raw materials for these textiles are chosen because their properties are suitable.

In your study of textiles, you will also learn the importance of design to make textiles look good and express individuality. Your study will increase your knowledge of textiles, and help you to choose wisely in the future.

EXTRAS

1. Write down a list of ceremonies that take place each year. Then write down what part textiles play in each ceremony.

2. Choose a period of history that interests you, and investigate the textiles used in this period. What were the main features of **a)** clothing or **b)** home furnishings?

Sources of Textiles

What are textiles made from? If you look closely at the surface of a piece of fabric, using a magnifying glass, a hand lens or a microscope, you will see some very fine 'hairs'. These are called **fibres** and they form the basis of all textiles.

Fig. 1.5

In your textile technology area, there should be some scraps of fabric. Working in pairs, choose a few scraps that vary in their appearance and texture. Using a pin, tease out a few fibres from the fabric. Place them on a microscope slide, put a drop of glycerol on top, and cover them with a coverslip. Look at the fibres under the microscope and make drawings of what you see. The surface of one fibre will be quite different from that of another. How would you describe the fibres – smooth, rough, scaly, long, short? The fibres vary because they come from different sources. Their differing properties help you to classify them.

Sources of fibres

In previous centuries, all fibres came from natural sources – the local plants and animals. Fibres from **vegetable sources** include **cotton** and **linen**. Cotton comes from the cotton plant – the fibres surround the seeds in the cotton boll. Linen comes from the stalks of the flax plant. The fibres from **animal sources** include **wool** and **silk**. Wool comes from sheep, goats and rabbits in the form of fleece or hair. Silk comes from the grub of the silkworm which makes a cocoon from the silk filament produced in its body. Cotton, linen, wool and silk are called **natural fibres** because they come from natural sources.

Fig. 1.6 shows the fibres of cotton, linen, wool and silk under a microscope. Even though they are all natural fibres, they are quite different from each other. The differences give the fibres their own properties, making them suitable for a variety of uses.

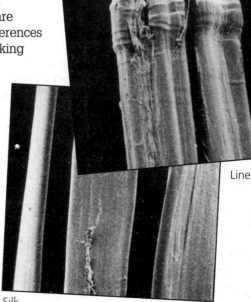

Cotton

Fig. 1.6

Linen

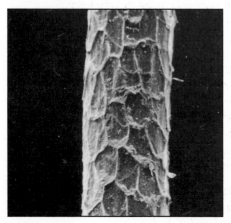

Wool

Silk

Draw up a table with a column for each of the natural fibres shown in Fig. 1.6. In each column, list textile items which you think could be made from a fabric of that particular fibre. Then, try to identify the reasons why you think that particular fibre is the most suitable for that textile item.

Cotton

Cotton is a very important plant fibre. Over 50 per cent of the world's fibres used for clothing is cotton. The cotton plant is thought to have originated in India. It was described as 'wool growing on bushes', hence the name 'cotton wool'. The fluffy fibres are called the cotton boll (see Fig. 1.7), which develops from the flowers when they turn to seed. When the fibres are picked, they dry out and look like twisted ribbon. However, they easily absorb water to become fluffy again. The absorbency of cotton is one of its properties, making it particularly suitable for nappies, towels and sportswear. Other properties include warmth, strength (when wet or dry), ability to withstand high temperatures, and ability to be bleached and dyed. However, it is also highly flammable, it creases easily, and it can be attacked by mildew (a type of mould that rots cotton). It is possible to treat cotton to improve these properties.

Look at the labels in your clothes to see how much cotton is used to make them. Can you estimate how much of all your clothing contains cotton? You could find out about some of the special 'finishes' applied to cotton. Fig. 1.8 shows a selection of clothes made from cotton.

Fig. 1.7

Fig. 1.8

Fig. 1.9

Linen

Linen comes from the stem of the flax plant, and is one of the oldest known natural fibres. It has been discovered that the Ancient Egyptians spun flax fibres. Nowadays, linen is considered expensive to produce, so it tends to be mixed with cheaper artificial fibres for clothing and household furnishings. The flax plant grows in damp conditions – in Ireland and Belgium, for example. Under the microscope, the stems look like bamboo. The properties of linen include strength (when wet or dry), absorbency, being hardwearing, and being cool to wear. As with cotton, linen is flammable, it creases easily and it can be attacked by mildew.

Linen was more popular in your grandparents' younger days. Ask someone from their generation what items in their home were made from linen.

Fig. 1.10

Wool

Wool is the most important animal fibre, and the wool industry has been important in Britain for many centuries. Wool is mainly produced from the fleece of sheep, and different breeds of sheep give different qualities of wool. The better qualities are the longer fibres from Merino sheep (see Fig. 1.10). They are reared in Australia and New Zealand. Wool, as a fibre, is three times more expensive to produce than cotton, owing to the fact that it is much more costly to rear animals than it is to grow crops.

Wool fibres are spun into yarn in woollen mills before being woven into fabric. Fig. 1.11 shows wool fibres being combed before being spun. Some wool fibres are fine and long, making them suitable for clothing, while the short and coarse fibres are more suitable for making carpets. Fig. 1.12 shows wool being woven to make a carpet.

Fig. 1.11

Fig. 1.12

Look at the labels in some items of clothing and see if you can find the Woolmark. Copy it on to a piece of paper, together with the special washing instructions necessary to keep wool looking like new.

Fig. 1.13 The Woolmark

If you look at wool under a microscope (see Fig. 1.6 on page 8) you can see the overlapping scales on the surface of the fibre. Air is trapped between the scaly fibres giving wool its most important property of warmth. Other properties include absorbency, elasticity and flame-resistance. Its disadvantages are that it can be attacked by moths, and it can shrink unless it is treated.

Silk

Silk is the most expensive of the natural fibres, and has always been associated with the wealthy. Silk comes from the cocoon of the silkworm (see Fig. 1.14). The worm spins the cocoon from a substance produced in its body, which is forced through two holes in its head in one long fibre. This is called a **filament**, and it can be over a kilometre in length. Silk is the only natural fibre to form a filament. The other natural fibres are short, and they are known as **staple fibres**. Silk is a very smooth fibre, as you can see from Fig. 1.6 on page 8.

Fig. 1.15 Silk being processed in a factory

Fig. 1.14

The business of farming silkworms is called sericulture. It is mainly carried out in China and Japan, as it has been for the past four thousand years. In spite of the fact that silk is fine and lightweight, its properties include warmth, strength, absorbency, the ability to drape well and shininess. Its disadvantages are that it is flammable, it needs careful washing, and it is damaged by perspiration and sunlight. It is also very expensive.

Artificial fibres

In the early 1900s, people tried to imitate silk by developing a fibre-forming liquid that could be forced through holes, to form a long filament. The device with holes was called a spinneret. It wasn't until the 1920s that commercial production of artificial fibres really began, and nylon was invented in 1938. Fig. 1.16 shows the first 'nylons'.

Artificial fibres can be subdivided into **regenerated fibres** and **synthetic fibres**. The difference is that regenerated fibres consist of a natural raw material, such as cellulose, which has undergone a chemical process, whereas synthetic fibres, such as nylon and polyester, are made entirely from chemicals. The desirable properties of artificial fibres include crease-resistance, lack of absorbency (making them quick to dry) and strength. Most artificial fibres are thermoplastic which means that they can be heat-set (permanently pleated).

Fig. 1.16

No one fibre seems to possess every desirable quality. It was soon discovered that blending fibres is an ideal way of achieving a near perfect result. Having looked at many labels in clothes, you will have discovered the importance of blending fibres. Look at the proportion of polyester to cotton in most shirts. What will the combined properties of these fibres be? Find out some other common blends of fibres and consider their properties.

Fibres to Fabrics

You have read about the range of fibres and their properties, but fibres cannot be used just as they are. First, they have to be made into a yarn which can then be made into a fabric. The fibres are combed into parallel lines. Then they are stretched and twisted into a long length of yarn. This process is called **spinning**.

Spinning

Hand spinning is an ancient craft, still used today in some parts of the world, such as South America and India. In Britain, spinning is a popular hobby for many people. Some people rear different varieties of sheep and prepare the fleece for spinning and dyeing. If there is a small amount of raw wool in your textile technology area, or if you are able to collect some from a hedgerow, try stretching and twisting the fibres. You will be surprised at the strength of the yarn you make.

A hand spindle was the first method of spinning, followed by the spinning wheel. In 1765, a spinning machine called a 'spinning jenny' was invented by James Hargreaves. Ask if your teacher can arrange for a visitor to come into school to demonstrate hand spinning, and how to use a spinning wheel. You may be able to try it for yourself. It may be possible for you to visit an Industrial Museum to see some of the developments in the textile industry.

Fig. 1.17 Hand spinning in France

Fig. 1.18

Fig. 1.19

Making yarn into fabric

The spun yarn is then made into fabric by various methods, the main ones being weaving and knitting. Less common methods include lace making (see Fig. 1.19), crochet and macramé.

Weaving

Weaving is an ancient craft – fragments of woven cloth have been found in the Egyptian Pharaohs' tombs. The basic principle of weaving is to overlap and underlap yarns at right angles to each other. The vertical yarns are held parallel and taut, and are called the **warp** threads. The horizontal yarn that passes under and over these warp threads at right angles is called the **weft**. If the weft passes over a warp, then under a warp, and so on, it is called a **plain weave**. Several patterned weaves can be created by passing the weft under and over a different number of warp threads (see Fig. 1.21).

Fig. 1.20

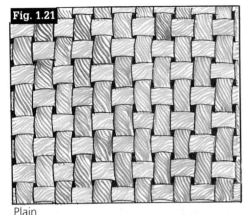

Fig. 1.21

Plain

Twill

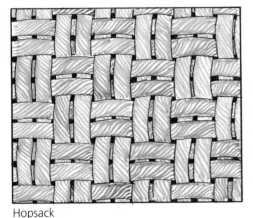

Hopsack

Herringbone

Make a simple weaving loom by cutting grooves in both ends of a piece of card. Wind some knitting yarn over the card so that the threads sit in the grooves. These are your warp threads. Now wind some knitting yarn around a thin strip of card so that it can pass over and under your warp threads. This is your weft. The edges are kept firm as the yarn is passed over and under at the sides. In commercial weaving, this is known as the selvedge or 'self-neatened edge'. Now you have your simple loom, try some of the patterned weaves illustrated in Fig. 1.21.

Modern weaving looms

Modern weaving looms power the weft between the warp threads in a water jet, doing away with the need for a shuttle to carry the weft across. You could organise a group topic to investigate the development of the textile mills during the Industrial Revolution. Imagine you worked in one of the weaving sheds. What were the conditions like (see Fig. 1.57)? Compare them with the modern weaving sheds (see Fig. 1.22). Another comparison could be with the child labour that is still used today in some parts of the world to produce intricately designed carpets for the home.

Fig. 1.22

Knitting

Knitting, like weaving, is an ancient craft, first done by hand with sharpened sticks for needles. The first knitting machines were invented in the 16th century. Fig. 1.23 shows the Little Rapid Knitting Machine which was first introduced into Britain in 1871. Knitting machines have developed over the years – they can now be computer-controlled (see Fig. 1.24).

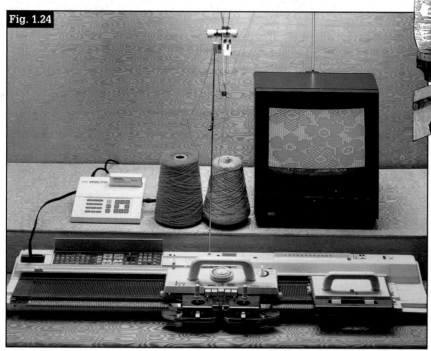
Fig. 1.24

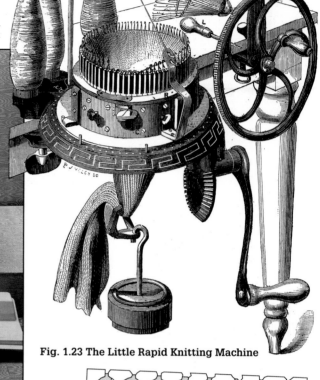
Fig. 1.23 The Little Rapid Knitting Machine

The principle of knitting is the interlocking of loops using one yarn (as opposed to two yarns in weaving). There are two kinds of knitting – **weft knitting** and **warp knitting**. Weft knitting is done by taking the yarn across the row, as in hand and some machine knitting. It is easy to unravel and it ladders, but it also has great elasticity. Knitwear and jersey fabrics are made in this way. Warp knitting is achieved by interlocking vertical loops with the loops on either side. This makes warp knitting firmer and less elastic, and it doesn't ladder.

Flat filament nylon yarn is often made in this way, and is used for underwear. Dress and shirting fabrics can also be warp knitted. Take a close look at the clothes in your wardrobe, and try to identify which ones have been woven, weft-knitted and warp-knitted.

Hand knit a small sample by casting on 20 stitches and knitting 10 rows. Ask your teacher to help if you haven't knitted before. If you can plain knit, try some patterned knitting using knit and purl stitches. If you have a knitting machine in your department, make a sample on it and compare your result with hand knitting for the time taken and the quality.

In D&T, you will learn to:
know that systems have inputs, processes and outputs and recognise these in a variety of simple styles
recognise pattern in the structure of objects
use computer-aided design and draughting techniques

Fig. 1.25 Knitted clothing

Designer knitwear

Fig. 1.26 shows a selection of designer knitwear from The Natural Dye Company. These have exciting and complicated designs, and use a range of colours. Another knitwear designer, Kaffe Fassett, is famous for his elaborate use of colour in his designs. He often uses up to 30 shades in a jumper. Can you find out about other knitwear designers? You can look out for their designs in the media, and on television programmes such as *The Clothes Show*.

Fig. 1.26

Fig. 1.27 (a) a pupil designing on a computer, (b) using a knitting machine, (c) machine-knitted fabric

Producing designs for knitwear can be great fun. In your technology department you may have software which will enable you to experiment with designing on a computer. Depending on your computer hardware, you may have programmes such as Mosaic, Artisan II, or Techtile Arc. The last software is compatible with an electronic knitting machine. If your school has one of these machines, you may be able to produce your design on it.

EXTRAS

1. Investigate the wide range of yarns available to the knitter. Try to collect some samples from family and friends, and weave or knit them into an interesting design. You could make it into a wall hanging for a present.

Applying Colour to Fabric

Why do you choose a particular fabric for your bedroom? Part of the reason may be that you like the design, but mainly you will choose it for the colour. Look at the colour wheel shown in Fig. 1.28. Generally speaking, the colours next to one another complement each other, while the colours on opposite sides of the wheel contrast with each other or even clash. Colours can create certain atmospheres, and you may choose a particular colour for a special occasion. Can you think of occasions that are marked by clothes of a certain colour, such as white for a Christian wedding or red for an Indian wedding? You may like to find out the origins of these traditions.

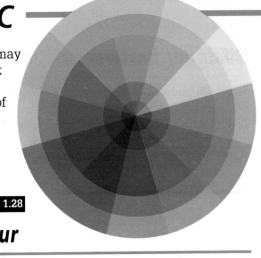

Fig. 1.28

Natural sources of colour

Colour has always been an important part of textile production. Evidence has been found of coloured fabric dating back to Ancient Egypt, 5000 years ago. Fabric was originally coloured only by natural substances, such as vegetables, fruit or plants. These were soaked in water, and the solution that formed was called a **dye**. The fabric was then soaked in the dye to change its colour. Depending on the area you lived in, different dyes could be produced. Lichens and heathers in Scotland produced the dyes used for tweed cloth. Cochineal comes from a beetle that lives on Mexican cactus plants. It gives bright red colours to silks and wool from that part of the world. The most expensive dye came from shellfish. It took 12 000 shellfish to produce 1 gram of dye which gave a wonderful purple colour. As it was so expensive, only kings and emperors could afford it, and it became known as 'royal purple'.

Lichen

Pine cone

Beetroot

Onions

Heather

Elder

Fig. 1.29 Natural sources of dye

Dyeing fabric

Fabric can be dyed at one of three stages during its production – at the fibre stage; when the fibres have been spun into yarn; or at the final cloth stage. Some fabrics do not take up dyes very well and the dyed fabric remains pale or fades very easily. To help prevent this from happening, a substance called a **mordant** is used in the dyeing process. First, the fabric is usually heated in a solution of mordant. Then, when the fabric is dyed, the mordant chemically fixes itself to the dye making it fast. This was discovered very early in the history of dyeing. Salt will act as a mordant, as will vinegar, copper filings, urine, wood ash, and a mixture of 4 teaspoons alum with 1 teaspoon cream of tartar.

In 1856, William Henry Perkin discovered that synthetic (artificial) dyes could be made from coal tars. Nowadays, synthetic dyes are used all the time, as the colours are very reliable. Can you think why synthetic dyes should be more reliable than natural ones?

	In D&T, you will learn to:
	estimate how long an activity might take, and the resources required and take this into account in your planning
	recognise the aesthetic qualities of natural and manufactured materials

Work in a group to do an experiment on dyeing fabrics. Some members of the group should collect scraps of natural and synthetic fabrics. These should be labelled with the fibre from which they are made – for example, wool. Other members of the group should collect some natural products which can be used to make dyes, such as onions, beetroot, mushrooms, spinach, marigolds, and privet. Each product needs to be soaked in water overnight. The next day, each product should be simmered for one hour. It can then be strained, and the liquid used as a dye. You may like to include a synthetic dye in your experiment, such as Dylon. Make an action plan for the practical session, and conduct your experiment by dyeing different fabrics in a selection of dyes. Record your results on a chart. What conclusions can you draw from this experiment?

Fig. 1.30

RESIST DYEING

Fabric can be decorated by a process known as **resist dyeing**. This means that when the fabric is dyed, certain parts of it 'resist' the dye because they are waxed or tied. These parts remain the original colour of the fabric.

Batik

One method of resist dyeing is called **batik** (see Fig. 1.30). You paint a design on to the fabric in hot wax, using a special tool called a tjanting (pronounced janting). The fabric is then dyed, but the dye does not penetrate the waxed areas of the fabric which remain the original colour. The process can be repeated by painting another design on to the fabric in hot wax, and dyeing the fabric a different colour. The end result is an attractive design in different colours. You can remove the wax by placing the fabric between sheets of newspaper and ironing it.

Tie dyeing

Another method of resist dyeing is **tie dyeing**. Various designs can be made by the fabric being tied in different ways. One method is to make a pattern of circles (see Fig. 1.31a). To do this, you pinch the centre of your piece of fabric with one hand and pull with the other to form a cone shape. Then you tie string tightly round the length of the fabric at regular intervals (see Fig. 1.31b). The fabric is then dyed. Another method of tie dyeing is to tie stones, or similar objects, into the fabric. Then you criss-cross thread tightly over the stones, and dye the fabric.

Fig. 1.31a

Fig. 1.31b

EXTRAS

1. Find out how fabric is dyed in the textile industry today.

2. In a group, discuss some of the reasons why most fabric manufactured in Britain is more expensive than fabric imported from other countries. You can find out which countries supply fabric by looking for a 'country of origin' label on the bales of fabric in a shop.

Decorating Textiles

The art of decorating textiles is as old as civilisation itself.

Embroidery

The Chinese produce heavily embroidered blouses and tablecloths. Many countries have developed their own traditional embroideries. One type of Indian embroidery is called **shishadur**. Strands of cotton in bright colours are used to stitch down shisha mirror glasses which decorate clothing, as you can see in Fig. 1.32. In India, embroidery is practised by women and men, and they decorate not only clothes but accessories and rugs, too.

Fig. 1.32

You could create an embroidery using the shishadur technique (see Fig. 1.33). Alternatively, using a piece of printed or resist-dyed fabric, you could decorate it with different textured yarns or metallic threads.

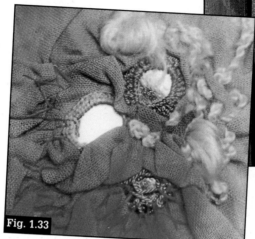
Fig. 1.33

Appliqué

You can decorate a piece of fabric or an item, such as a top or a bag, by using a technique called **appliqué**. This involves sewing on pieces of fabric, by hand or machine, to form a design. Fig. 1.34 shows the decoration of a quilt cover done in appliqué. As you can see from the photograph, not all the pieces of fabric are completely attached to the quilt which makes the design more interesting.

Fig. 1.34

Fig. 1.35

Fabric painting

Fabric painting can be done in several ways. You can use your fingers, a sponge, a paint brush or a diffuser to paint a pattern on to your fabric. Special fabric crayons which are made of non-toxic dye can be used to draw your design directly on to the fabric (see Fig. 1.35). The design is then 'heat set' by placing the fabric between two sheets of paper and ironing it for two minutes. The design should then be colour-fast when the fabric is washed.

Block printing

Block printing is an easy method of printing. Blocks can be made from materials such as potatoes, wood, cork, lino or cotton reels. The design which will be printed on to the fabric needs to be raised above the surface of the block, so the unwanted parts of the material are cut away as shown in Fig. 1.36. The raised surface is then painted with fabric paint, and placed firmly down on to the fabric which should be resting on a pad of newspaper. The process can then be repeated with the same block, or one with a different design, to produce an interesting pattern (see Fig. 1.37).

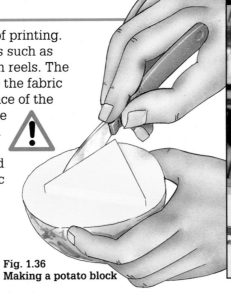

Fig. 1.36
Making a potato block

Fig. 1.37

Fig. 1.38

Screen printing

Screen printing involves using a stencil and a screen. You make a stencil by cutting your design out of newspaper with a craft knife. You must make sure that the edges of your design are cleanly cut so that the paint will not run. You make a screen by stretching a piece of fabric over a frame and stapling it in position. The fabric for this always used to be silk but, nowadays, it is more likely to be a synthetic fibre.

You should lay the fabric on a blanket or some paper. Then tape the stencil on to the outside of the screen attached to the frame. Turn the frame upside down and place it on top of the fabric where you want the design to print. Some dye and a squeezee are put in the base of the frame. As the squeezee is moved over the screen, the dye is forced through the fine mesh and the cut-out design of the stencil on to the fabric. When you have finished printing, you should carefully remove the frame, and leave the fabric to dry. You can repeat the process if you want a more complicated design.

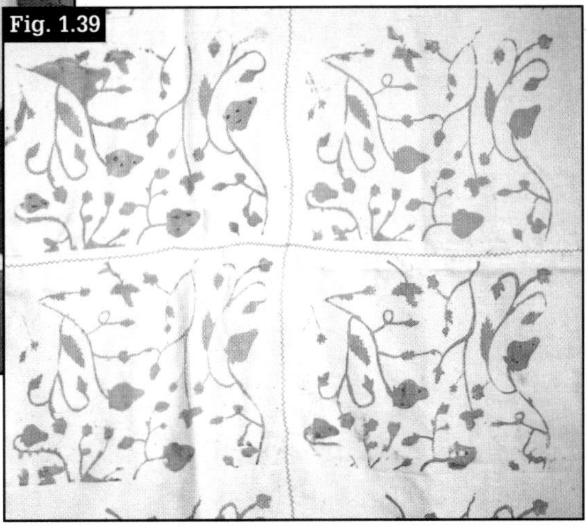

Fig. 1.39

Silk painting

Silk painting is a delicate form of resist dyeing. A liquid wax is used to outline the design. Then special silk paints are used to fill in the areas inside the waxed lines. You can achieve very artistic results with silk painting. You could mount small samples of silk painting on to card to make greetings cards.

EXTRAS

1. Investigate a range of traditional embroideries and crafts, and produce a sample of each of them.

2. Design a logo for a school club which could be done as embroidery or appliqué.

Textiles and Design

Design plays an important part throughout the production of textiles, from the fibre stage to the finished article. Fibre technologists are always trying to improve some aspect of the fabric that will be produced – its appearance, 'handle' (feel), durability, washability, cost, or particular special property. **Fabric designers** design the different patterns that will appear on the fabrics.

Fabric design

The design of a fabric needs to be suitable for its purpose. Designers for dress fabrics usually work with small-scale designs which look good whichever way the fabric is turned. Designers for curtain fabrics and upholstery often work with large – scale designs which need to look right hanging in long lengths, or on furniture. Most fabric designs are printed on to the material, but some are woven in using coloured yarns, for example tartan. Designs for carpets are all woven in. Fig. 1.40 shows a designer working on a carpet design.

Fig. 1.40

Fig. 1.41a

Whatever their purpose, the design of all fabrics is based on a repeated pattern. The image that is repeated can be very simple, such as a polka dot, or more complex, such as a spray of flowers. There are three basic arrangements of repeats. In **simple repeats** the lines of images are repeated directly below each other. In **half-brick repeats** the lines of images are staggered, like bricks in a wall (see Fig. 1.41a). In **scatter repeats** the images are apparently arranged randomly although, if you look carefully, you will see that this random arrangement is itself repeated (see Fig. 1.41b).

Fig. 1.41b

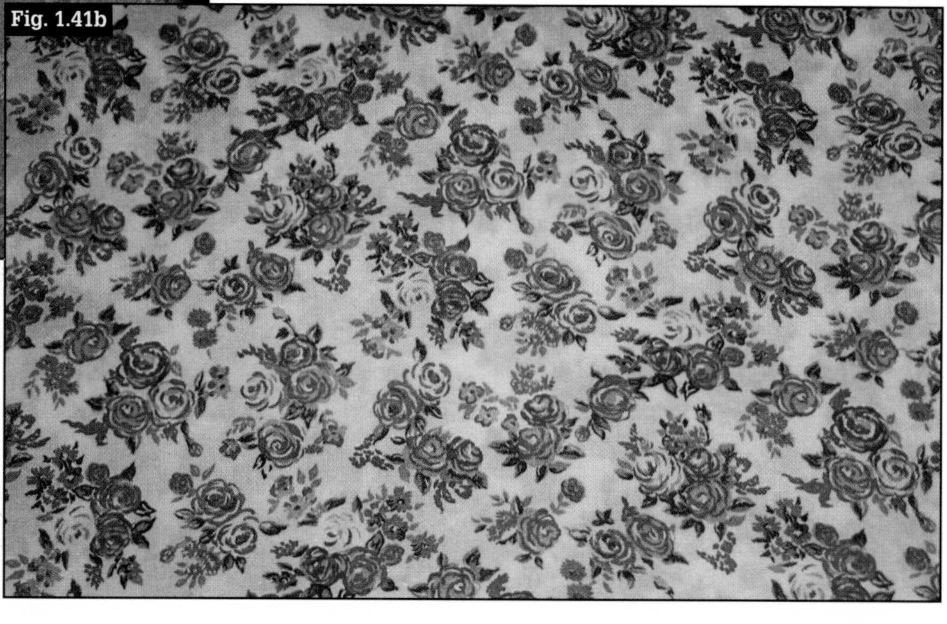

Clothes design

Fabric designers in industry work to a brief, just as you might in your Design & Technology projects. The brief may be supplied by the buyer in a large department store group, who is looking for new curtain materials or, in the case of dress fabrics, the brief may be from the **garment designer**. This is the person who designs the style of clothes.

You may choose to wear certain styles of clothing to express your individuality, or to give you a certain image. How important is it to you to feel part of the group by dressing in the same way as your friends?

Fig. 1.42 Teenagers often like to have a group image

Clothing styles change with fashion. This century has seen an increase in the number of fashion designers. Their work has been noticed more with the broadcasting of the British Fashion Show Awards, and programmes such as *The Clothes Show*. A fashion designer usually works for a fashion house, such as Dior or Chanel. They may produce 'one-off' exclusive designs known as **haute couture**, or 'off the peg' ready-to-wear designs called **pret à porter**. Designer clothes have also become more accessible to a larger number of people. Large chain stores have their own fashion designers, for example, George at Asda. Can you name any others?

Fig. 1.43 Modelling at a clothes show

Computer-aided design

In industry, designers have the use of a **computer-aided design** (CAD) system. This involves designing on a computer. The designs can be stored, and altered later, if necessary. Full-colour graphics give the designer a good idea of what the finished article will look like. You may have a CAD system in your department. If so, you could experiment with designing on it. Fig. 1.44 shows a designer using CAD for a carpet design.

Fig. 1.44

EXTRAS

1. Choose a decade in this century, and research the main fashion trends and famous designers of that decade. Has their influence lasted, and made an impact on today's clothes styles?

Interior design

Just as clothes may reflect your personality, so the interior design of your home may tell other people quite a lot about your tastes and preferences. Over recent years, people have created a demand for coordinated home furnishings. Fig. 1.45 shows a bedroom with matching bedspreads and curtains, and wallpaper and a carpet that tone in with the fabric. Some shops like Marks & Spencer, Next and Laura Ashley stock coordinated furnishings, including matching wallpaper.

Fig. 1.45

Fig. 1.46

Interior designing involves harmonising the colour and style of your furnishings to achieve the desired effect. Fig. 1.46 shows a conservatory with furnishings in shades of blue and green which help to create a cool atmosphere in the light, airy room. In contrast with this, Fig. 1.47 shows a dining room with furnishings in red, helping to create a warm atmosphere in the room.

Imagine that you are able to redesign a room in your home. What would you have to consider? Sketch your ideas and collect samples if possible.

Fig. 1.47

22

Sources for designs

When you are designing, you may well use your imagination to produce a design. Sources of inspiration for designs are endless, for example, natural objects, such as shells or plants, or architectural features, such as archways. The designer in Fig. 1.48 is using geometric shapes for her design.

Fig. 1.48

Fig. 1.49

Fig. 1.49 shows a design that was inspired by a picture. The designer copied the picture on to graph paper, using coloured pencils. Then she reproduced the picture as embroidery, using the design drawn on the graph paper as a guide.

Fig. 1.50 shows cushions, pillow cases, pictures and wall hangings which have been produced by pupils using various sources for their designs.

Fig. 1.50

Textiles and the Consumer

In this chapter you have learned about the importance of fibre properties, design and colour when choosing and making textile items. But what about their performance? Do they carry out the function they were intended to perform as either an item for the home or an article of clothing? Other important factors that may influence you in the purchase of textiles are advertising, the method of shopping and the method of payment. Every time you buy goods you are a **consumer**. As a consumer, you have certain rights and responsibilities. You can complain if the goods you buy do not meet the required standard.

Advertising

When you want to choose a new item of clothing, what are you influenced by? Apart from being able to afford it, are you influenced by advertising, designer labels, your friends' opinions, or window displays? All of these probably have a part to play in your decision-making process.

In a group, collect a range of clothing advertisements. Why do they appeal to you do you think? Is it the personality wearing it, his/her age or sex, the style, the designer label, or the availability of the shop where it is sold? Carry out a survey on your friends and family, to find out why the advertisements you have collected appeal to them, and record your results in a bar chart.

Fig. 1.51 An advertisement for Levi jeans

Labelling for clothes

Look inside any item of clothing you possess and you should almost always be able to find a label. The system of **care labelling** has developed over recent years, and is invaluable to the consumer. Labels should tell you the size of the garment, the make, the country of origin, the fibre content and the care instructions. Fig. 1.52a shows a label from a jumper. Fig. 1.52b shows what some of the care instruction symbols mean.

MADE IN THE U.K.

TO FIT CHEST
33in

TOUR DE POITRINE
85cm

front

Fig. 1.52a A clothes label for a jumper

Fig. 1.52b Care instruction symbols

 may be tumble dried

 do not tumble dry

warm iron (an iron with one dot means cool, an iron with three dots means hot)

 do not iron

 do not dry clean

100% ACRYLIC/ACRYLIQUE

WARM

COLD RINSE
RESHAPE WHILE DAMP
DRY FLAT AWAY
FROM DIRECT HEAT
COOL IRON WHEN DRY
RINCER A L'EAU FROIDE
REMETTRE EN FORME
, ENCORE HUMIDE
SECHER A PLAT LOIN D'UNE
SOURCE DE CHALEUR
REPASSER SEC A FER DOUX
H   CA 01295

back

 white cotton and linen articles without special finishes

 cotton, linen or viscose, articles without special finishes where colours are fast at 60°C

 nylon; polyester/cotton mixtures; polyester, cotton and viscose articles with special finishes; cotton/acrylic mixtures

 cotton, linen or viscose articles where colours are fast at 40°C but not at 60°C

 wool, wool mixed with other fibres, silk

 handwash (do not machine wash)

 do not wash

 may be dry cleaned

In D&T, you will learn to:
propose modifications to improve the performance and appeal of existing products
know that the aesthetic qualities influence cosumers' choices
identify markets for goods and services
recognise that a solution may result in problems in other areas
calulate costs and make decisions on price

Choosing clothes

You probably have more money to spend on clothes than your parents did. As well as more money, you have a much greater choice of clothes compared with previous generations. Where do you choose to shop, and why? You could carry out a survey on the shops in your area to find out what types of clothes they sell, for what age group, and whether or not the clothes are expensive. Are you prepared to travel a long distance to your favourite shop?

Perhaps you prefer to buy your clothes in the comfort of your own home. **Mail order shopping** began in the 1920s, and has changed its image considerably over the years. Major high street stores offer a mail order service, and the recently introduced facility of being able to order by telephone has also improved the service. Some members of your class may be able to bring a mail order catalogue into school. You could choose an item of

Fig. 1.53 A variety of clothes stores

clothing you like from the catalogue, and compare its cost with that of a similar item in your local shop. What are the advantages and disadvantages of mail order shopping to different members of the family?

Methods of payment

In the same way that you have a choice of shops for your clothes, you also have a variety of ways you can pay for them. Most people not only have a bank account, but they also have **credit cards**, such as Access and Visa, and **charge cards** from High Street stores, such as British Home Stores, Marks & Spencer, House of Fraser, etc.

Consumer protection

As a consumer, you are protected by law against faulty goods under the Sale of Goods Act, 1979. This states that goods should be of an acceptable (merchantable) quality, be as described and fit for the purpose for which they were intended. If they do not meet these standards, you can take the goods back to the shop together with the receipt, and the shopkeeper will either refund your money or replace the faulty article.

Advertisers also have to ensure they do not mislead the consumer, and make any false claims. Under the Trades Description Act, 1968, it is an offence to display a misleading advertisement, and any complaints can be reported to the local Trading Standards Department.

Safety standards for textiles

Textile technology is about meeting people's needs. To give you, the consumer, the best possible choice, the properties of textiles are constantly being improved. Safety is an important issue, particularly the flame-resistance of textiles – for example, fabrics for children's nightwear undergo strict tests to ensure their safety. Fabrics for the upholstery of furniture also undergo tests for flame-resistance (see Fig. 1.54). When a fabric passes the test, it is given the British Standard 5722. You may see this on a label on children's nightwear.

EXTRAS

1. You could carry out a survey on the many methods of payment for goods to discover their advantages and disadvantages.

2. In a group, role play a situation that could arise between a shop assistant and a consumer who is returning faulty goods.

3. Draw up a table comparing the monthly rates of interest charged by credit card companies and in-store charge accounts. You could use a computer database to record your data.

Fig. 1.54 Upholstery being tested for flame-resistance

The Textile Industry

The textile industry has undergone revolutionary technological changes in its history.

Sewing machines

Fig. 1.55

Fig. 1.55 shows Jones's sewing machine which was used in the nineteenth century. Compare it with one of today's latest developments shown in Fig. 1.56 – the computerised sewing machine. It looks very complex but, in fact, it is very easy to use and maintain. It is controlled by a microchip. The spool is wound straight from the needle, and the stitches are made by lightly pressing a touch pad with your foot. A sequence of stitches can be programmed in the machine's memory, so a process that is repeated is identical to the one before. The machine can be fitted with an overlocker which is mainly used on stretch fabrics. It machines, neatens and trims a seam in one process, so it is very useful to the textile industry. You may have a computerised or electric sewing machine in your school which you could use.

Knitting machines

Computerised knitting machines are also available, and offer enormous design potential for the machine knitter. Fig. 1.24 on page 14 shows one of these machines. You design on a screen which is then 'read' by the machine. Designs can be altered, reversed and repeated, etc. If you have a computerised knitting machine in your school your teacher may be able to arrange a demonstration on it. (For more information on knitting see pages 14–15.)

Developments in the textile industry

Originally, clothes were all made at home. The natural fibres were spun into yarn, and the yarn was then woven or knitted into fabric, from which clothes were made – it was a cottage industry. It wasn't until the nineteenth century that machinery was developed to weave yarn into cloth. Weaving sheds, like the one shown in Fig. 1.57, were built, and the textile industry expanded rapidly, racing ahead to keep pace with technological developments. Fig. 1.22 on page 13 shows a modern highly sophisticated weaving loom.

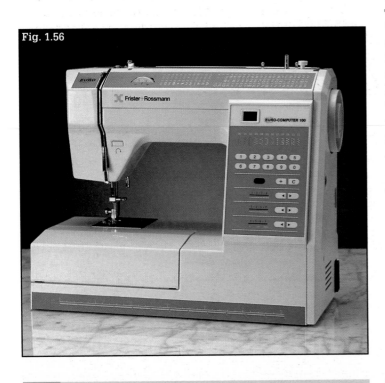

Fig. 1.56

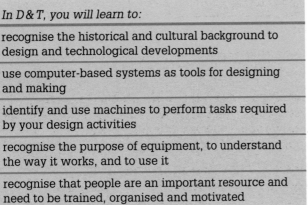

In D&T, you will learn to:

recognise the historical and cultural background to design and technological developments

use computer-based systems as tools for designing and making

identify and use machines to perform tasks required by your design activities

recognise the purpose of equipment, to understand the way it works, and to use it

recognise that people are an important resource and need to be trained, organised and motivated

Fig 1.57 A weaving shed in use during the Industrial Revolution

Modern technological developments

Recent technological developments have transformed the textile industry. The British textile industry has experienced difficulties in competing with cheaper imports from abroad. Foreign labour costs are much lower than British costs, so the British textile industry has had to be streamlined to make it competitive again. Modern technology has saved the day, and you can see evidence of it at every stage, from design to manufacture.

Fig.1.58 A computer-controlled pattern cutter

Designers

Designers use **computer-aided design** (CAD) systems to design on screen. You may have access to a CAD system, or computer software such as Artisan II or Superart, in which case you could practise your skills as a designer using a computer.

Pattern cutters

Computers are also used during the manufacture of garments. They control machines such as pattern cutters. This is called **computer-aided manufacture** (CAM). Pattern shapes are stored in the computer's memory, and can be dragged around the screen to give the most economical layout for the fabric. When you cut out fabric, it tends to be only single or double layers but, in industry, computer-controlled cutting machines can cut out many layers of fabric at once.

Garment makers

Garment makers are highly skilled machinists who usually complete only one process in the make-up of garments. Some machinists complete the whole garment from start to finish, but it usually takes longer even though it is less monotonous. Separating out tasks is called **division of labour**, and it is very common in industries producing goods by mass production. Nowadays, garment makers use highly sophisticated technological machines.

Your school may have an industry link with a textile firm in which case your teacher may be able to arrange a visit. Alternatively, it may be possible for an industrialist to come and talk to you about technological developments in the textile industry. You could find out what qualifications you need to have to work in different parts of the textile industry.

Fig. 1.59 Garment makers

EXTRAS

1. Investigate the importance of a logo in advertising a company. Imagine that you are the managing director of a textile company that makes swimwear, for instance. Design a logo for your company. If possible, make it on a computerised sewing machine.

2. Write down the most useful features of a machine used for
a) computer-aided design, or b) computer-aided manufacture.

2 GRAPHIC MEDIA

Graphic media are anything that can be used to create a drawing, a painting or a picture. Pencils, pens, markers, paint, cameras and even some computer software packages are all examples of graphic media. The following pages will help you to choose a medium which is suitable for the work you are doing. For example, you would not normally use charcoal for a detailed working drawing. However, it is an excellent material to use for a study into the effects of light and shade.

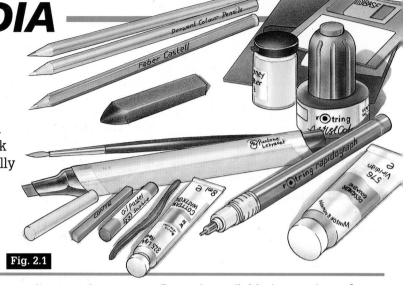

Fig. 2.1

Paper

There are many different types of paper available, but for most of your drawing work you will probably use cartridge paper. This paper is excellent for general drawing and is particularly good for pencil and ink drawings. Many designers do their rough work on thin paper called **layout paper.**

If you put a wet medium, such as watercolour or poster paint, on to cartridge paper the paper will become bumpy. Therefore, when you are working with a wet medium you will need to use a heavier and more absorbent paper. Also, you will need to stretch the paper before you use it so that it remains flat (see Fig. 2.2).

Paper is available in a variety of different sizes, weights and textures. It can be bought in a range of sizes known as the 'A' series. A0 is the largest and A6 the smallest. You have probably used A3 and A4 paper before. If you look at Fig. 2.3 you will see that A3 is twice as big as A4, A2 is twice as big as A3, and so on. The largest size, A0, measures 1189 mm × 841 mm – the area of one square metre.

Fig. 2.2 Stretching paper

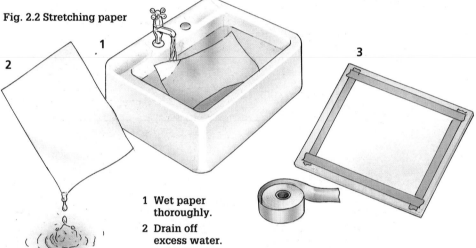

1 Wet paper thoroughly.
2 Drain off excess water.
3 Stick to a clean board with gummed tape.

Fig. 2.3 The 'A' series paper sizes

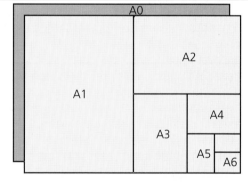

If you look at the label on the end of a new packet of paper in your school you will probably see the letters 'gsm' after a number. It might be '80 gsm', for example. This is the weight of the paper shown in grams per square metre. The weight of the paper is a guide to how thick it is. The thicker the paper, the more it weighs. Thin layout paper weighs 45 gsm while cartridge paper might weigh 120 gsm.

The texture of the paper, its roughness, is known as the **tooth**. Smooth papers are good for fine line work but rougher papers, with more tooth, are used for pastel or charcoal work.

Fig. 2.4

	In D&T, you will learn to:
	work with a variety of media to produce graphic outcomes
	aim for a high quality of accuracy and presentation
	recognise the purpose of different types of equipment, to understand their handling characteristics, and the basic principles upon which they work

Pencils

We sometimes call pencils 'lead pencils' but in fact they contain graphite not lead. Traditional pencils have a wooden case glued around the graphite core. Pencils are graded according to their hardness or softness. There are many different grades ranging from 9H, which is very hard, to EE, which is extremely soft. Soft pencils, such as 3B or 4B, are good for sketching and shading. Very soft pencils can be messy, so you should experiment before using them on an important piece of work.

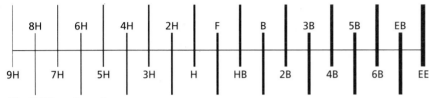

Fig. 2.6 Pencil grades

	8H		6H		4H		2H		F		B		3B		5B		EB	
9H		7H		5H		3H		H		HB		2B		4B		6B		EE

A **clutch pencil** looks similar to a plastic biro but contains lead instead of ink. The fine lead clutch pencil has a very thin lead made of polymer and graphite. These leads are usually half a millimetre thick but they can be as thin as 0.3 mm. Clutch pencils always give the same thickness of line and do not need to be sharpened.

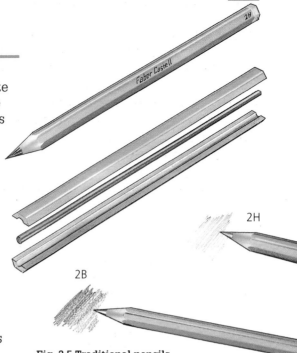

Fig. 2.5 Traditional pencils

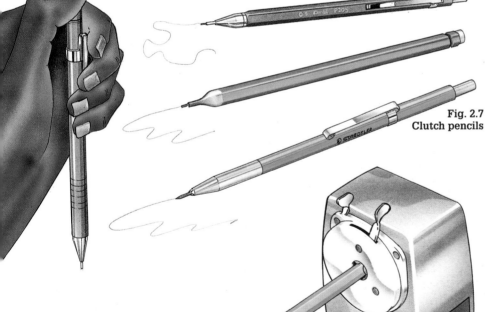

Fig. 2.7 Clutch pencils

Which pencil you use depends on what you are doing. For sketching use a traditional pencil, and for making accurate technical or working drawings use a fine lead clutch pencil. You should use a plastic rubber for correcting any mistakes. Other types of rubbers may mark and crease your paper, especially if they are dirty.

Sharpening pencils

Pencils need to be kept sharp. There may be a sharpener fixed to a desk in your classroom or you may have a small sharpener of your own. You can also use a small piece of glass paper to keep a sharp point on your pencil (see Fig. 2.8).

Fig. 2.8 Pencil sharpeners

Take care when sharpening your pencil with a **craft knife**. Always cut away from you.

EXTRAS

1. Find three types of paper, of different weight and texture. Using hard and soft pencils see how many types of marks and tones you can draw. What differences are there between the papers? Which is the best for pencil drawing?

Coloured pencils

Using coloured pencils is an easy way to apply colour to your drawings. A solid area of colour can be produced by keeping the pencil at a low angle to the paper and using the side of the lead rather than just the point.

Some coloured pencils are soluble in water and give a similar effect to watercolour. You draw on the paper with your pencil and then lightly brush your pencil marks with a clean, wet brush. These water-soluble pencils are less messy than watercolours.

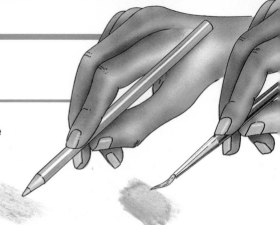

Fig. 2.9 Water-soluble coloured pencils

Charcoal

Charcoal is one of the oldest drawing materials. It is made by burning twigs of willow in a kiln. Charcoal is now sold as either sticks or made into charcoal pencils. To achieve the best effect you should use a fairly strong, rough paper. Do not use your plastic rubber with charcoal as it will get very dirty and may then spoil your pencil work. You should use a **kneaded** or **putty** rubber. You can also use charcoal as a background for a drawing, as shown in Fig. 2.10. You shade in an area of the paper using the charcoal and then with a kneaded rubber 'draw' into the shaded area.

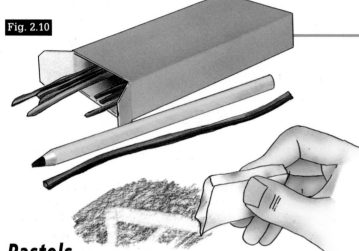

Fig. 2.10

Pastels

Pastels can be used to give soft, fresh and bright colours. They are made from powdered colour pigment stuck together with a weak gum or paste. There are three different grades of hardness – soft, medium and hard. You can buy pastels as sticks (similar to coloured chalks), as rectangular blocks, or in pencil form.

Pastels do not work very well on smooth paper but rougher paper with a tooth is ideal. Sugar paper is suitable or you can buy paper specially made for pastels. Pastels can be used like chalk and drawn straight on to the paper, or they can be scraped into a powder and then rubbed on to the paper using your finger (see Fig. 2.11).

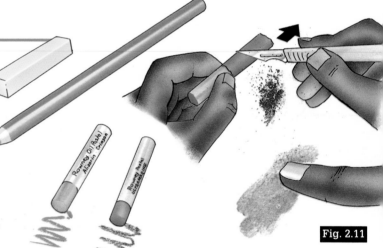

Fig. 2.11

Protecting your work

Fig. 2.12

Pastel and charcoal drawings are very delicate and smudge very easily. To stop this happening the drawings need to be fixed. As soon as a drawing is finished it should be sprayed with a clear liquid known as fixative. These fixatives can be bought either in an aerosol can or in a small bottle. Some people do not like using aerosols, and instead use a sprayer which you blow through (see Fig. 2.12).

Take care with fixatives. Always use them in a well-ventilated area. Avoid spraying them close to or into your mouth and eyes. It is a good idea to ask your teacher for help before you do this.

Pastel drawings can still be damaged even after fixing, so it is a good idea to put a sheet of tissue or greaseproof paper over your work before you put it in your folder.

Marker pens

There are two different kinds of marker pens used for graphic work. You are already familiar with the felt-tip pen which uses water-based ink. The tips of the pens are either rounded or chisel-shaped. Water-based ink takes a minute or two to dry, so you must be careful not to smudge it. The other type of marker can usually be recognised by its smell. It uses spirit-based ink which dries very quickly, and is often known as a graphic or studio marker. Spirit-based markers have a much wider range of colours than the water-based type and most of them can be refilled when they run out. You will need to work quickly with this type of marker otherwise the ink will dry and leave a striped effect on your work. Sometimes the ink spreads out over the outlines of your drawing or soaks through the paper. To stop this happening you will need a special **bleed-proof** paper. Ask your teacher about this.

Always use spirit-based markers in a well-ventilated area and avoid breathing in the fumes.

Fig. 2.13

Ink pens and brushes

You can draw with ink straight from the bottle, using a pen or a fine brush. You can also mix it with water, and with a brush use it as a wash to cover a large area. Simple pens, fitted with metal nibs which are dipped directly into the ink, can be used but they need refilling every few minutes. Drawing pens fitted with an ink cartridge are much less messy, and there is no ink bottle to knock over. For accurate drawings a technical pen can be used. This has a hollow needle instead of a metal nib. A technical pen can produce very fine, accurate lines which are all the same width.

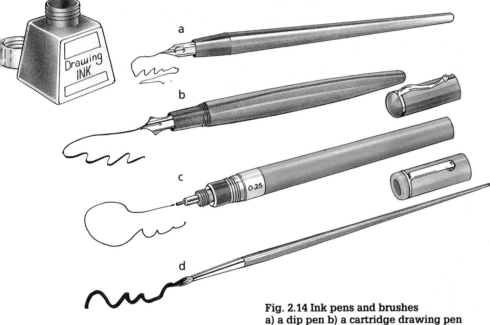

Fig. 2.14 Ink pens and brushes
a) a dip pen b) a cartridge drawing pen
c) a technical pen d) a fine ink brush

Poster paint and watercolours

Poster paint and gouache are opaque forms of water-based paint. They can be used when you want to paint over your drawing completely, so that your drawing does not show through. Poster paint can be used on most types of paper, card and even wood. Watercolour is very similar to poster paint except that you can see through it. It is used to provide thin transparent washes of colour that allow a drawing to show through. Watercolours are usually painted on special watercolour paper which is quite thick and absorbs the water easily. Remember that your paper will distort when you use wet media so you must stretch it before you start work.

Fig. 2.15 Using watercolour

Computer Graphics

Computer systems like the one shown in Fig. 2.17 can be used to produce graphic work. You are able to draw using either the keyboard or a **mouse**. It is possible to draw on the screen with a mouse in the same way as you draw with a pencil on paper.

Fig. 2.17 A computer system

Fig. 2.18 An example of graphics software

Software

Writing computer programs for graphics can be quite complicated and so it is a good idea to use one which is already available. These ready-made programs are known as software. Ask your teacher to show you the graphics software for the computers in your school. Most graphics software is stored on disc which is then loaded into the computer. Your work can be saved on to a hard or floppy disk so that you can add to it or change it at a later date.

Computer art

Computer art uses the computer screen as though it were an artist's canvas. You may have used this type of software already in school. The software allows you to change the colours of the tiny dots, called pixels, which make up the screen.

This method of producing computer graphics is known as **raster** or **pixel** graphics. It is possible to use a video camera that takes still photographs in computer artwork (see section on video cameras on page 35).

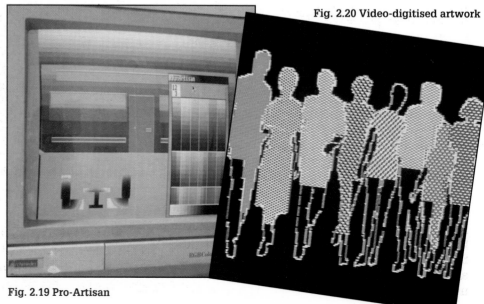

Fig. 2.20 Video-digitised artwork

Fig. 2.19 Pro-Artisan

In D & T, you will learn to:
know that systems have inputs, processes and outputs and recognise these in a variety of simple systems
select software for a task or application
identify clearly the requirements, and make correct use of information technology equipment, software and techniques in making presentations and reports

Computer-aided design

Computer-aided design (CAD) is a method of making design drawings using a particular type of graphics software. Some programs will allow you to design an object on the computer screen and then make it with the help of a computer-controlled machine. Software which produces technical or working drawings calculates a series of points and joins them with lines, as in Fig 2.21. Drawings produced in this way are called 'vector drawings'. Some of the more sophisticated programs allow items to be drawn and then displayed as three-dimensional objects.

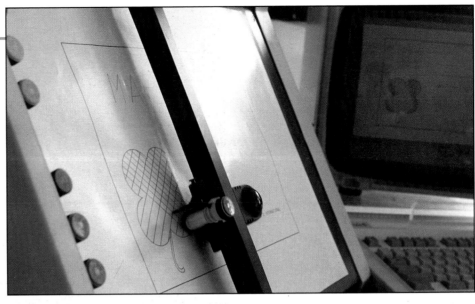

Fig. 2.21 Computer-aided design

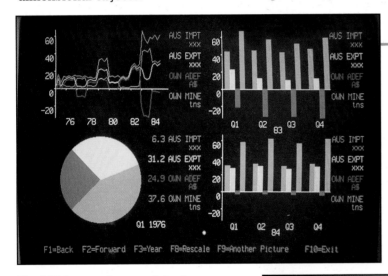

Fig. 2.22 A computer spreadsheet

Spreadsheet graphics

Computer spreadsheets allow you to handle and use information (also known as data). The information might be the contents of your bank account or the results of a survey you have carried out as part of your project work. Most spreadsheet software will allow you to display the information graphically once the information has been entered into the computer. Line graphs, bar charts, pie charts and scattergraphs can then be easily produced.

Fig. 2.23 A3 and A4 computer screens for desk top publishing

Desk top publishing

Desk top publishing (DTP) enables you to combine written information and graphics on your computer screen. It can be used to produce documents, posters, newspapers and signs. Text can be typed into a computer using a wordprocessing program, and pictures can be included in this text by using a scanner or a video digitiser. Most desk top publishing systems provide a wide range of different page layouts and styles of lettering. Some even include graphic symbols and page borders which can be used when needed.

EXTRAS

1. Make a collection of posters, leaflets, handbills and junk mail. Look carefully at the layout of the page, the text and the illustrations. Can you tell if they were produced by a computer graphics system?

Photography

Photography is a very useful graphic medium in Design & Technology. It allows you to record things quickly and accurately and can be used throughout the design process. You may want to take photographs as part of your investigation to help you identify opportunities for designing or to record the testing of your finished work. The final product of a project might take the form of a photograph or a piece of graphic work including several photographs.

Films and cameras

There are many different types of film available – colour, black and white, prints or slides. Your choice of film will depend on the camera that you are using and what you intend to do with the finished photographs. You must make sure that the film you use is suitable for the camera you are using. It is possible to buy 35 mm cassettes, 126 and 110 film cartridges, disc films and roll film. Film can be obtained to take either prints or slides. Slides are useful if you have to make a presentation to a group of people, but prints will be necessary if you are going to include photographs in your graphic work or in your folder.

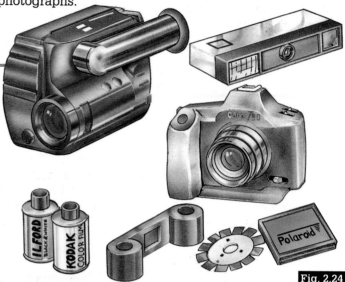

Fig. 2.24

Fig. 2.25

Taking photographs

Good results can be obtained with all types of cameras, providing you follow a few basic rules.

1 Make sure that there is enough light to take a photograph, especially if you are photographing indoors. If there is not enough natural light you may need to use a flash.

2 Try to ensure that the light source is behind you. It is not a good idea to take a photograph directly into the light, even with an automatic camera. The result may be a pale and rather hazy photograph.

3 Arrange the composition of the photograph carefully in the camera viewfinder before taking it. Take care not to cut off people's heads or include your thumb in the shot.

4 When taking a photograph hold the camera steady, and gently squeeze the shutter release.

When photographing out of school always check that you have permission to take a particular shot. Some people do not allow photographs to be taken without permission.

Developing your film

Once you have taken your photographs, your film needs to be developed or processed. You can do this by sending your film to a company which specialises in developing films or by taking it in to a shop which offers this service. If you have access to a dark room you can develop your own film. Ask your teacher if there is a dark room that you can use in school.

Instant photographs

One of the easiest ways of taking photographs is to use an instant camera. The films used in these cameras contain special chemicals which start developing the film as soon as a photograph is taken. Films for this type of camera are rather expensive, but you only have to wait a minute or two to see the photograph.

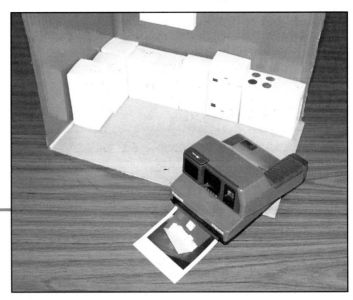
Fig. 2.26 A Polaroid camera developing a print

Fig. 2.27 A Canon still-video camera.

Video cameras

Video is another form of instant photography. It is possible with most video cameras to play back what you have filmed while you are still at the location. This allows you to make sure that you have filmed exactly what you needed. Video is an excellent medium for investigating how things work. Not only can you replay what you have recorded but you can also freeze one frame of the video. This allows you to study in detail what is happening.

Video cameras are now available which are capable of taking still photographs. A video digitiser converts the image into numerical information so that it can be fed into a computer. This photograph can then be used within a computer art program (see page 32).

Photocopiers

Photocopiers are very useful for graphic work in Design & Technology. They can be used to copy and enlarge drawings and photographs. You can use them to produce copies of documents such as questionnaires and reports. It is possible to buy **clip art books** which contain a variety of symbols, borders and lettering styles which you can photocopy and include in your graphic work to give it a professional look. Before copying anything, check that you are allowed to do so. Most publications have a copyright which makes it illegal for you to copy them without permission. Always check with your teacher first. Clip art books are copyright-free so you may copy them as much as you like.

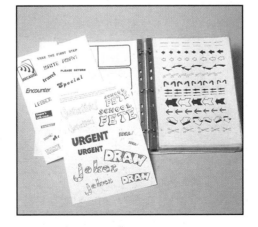
Fig. 2.28 Pages from a clip art book

The form of photography you choose will depend on the equipment that is available for you to use. Find out what is available in school. Is there a camera that you can use? Will you need permission to take it out of school? Do you know how to use it? You may have a camera of your own that you can use.

EXTRAS

1. Look back through this chapter at the graphic media covered. Make a list of other types of graphic media not mentioned in this chapter. For what kind of work would you use them?

3 SAFETY

Design & technology is not just about learning to design and make things. It is also about learning how to make your own decisions in a mature, adult way, and about being a responsible person. Taking some responsibility for your own safety, and for the safety of your friends, is very important. Safety depends upon your attitude and your behaviour. Accidents usually only happen when people are being careless or when somebody is fooling about. When you are careful and sensible, you will be safe.

How you dress

When you are using machines and equipment loose clothing, jewellery, ties and long hair can be dangerous. You should remove any jewellery, and tie back long hair. You should wear an apron or overall to protect your clothes, and wear stout shoes. Some things that you do may require special protective clothing and eye protection. Always wear the safety items provided, and make sure that they are looked after properly for the next person to use.

CHECK OUT THIS DUDE, HE AIN'T SO COOL — HOW MANY WAYS DOES HE BREAK THE RULE?

	In D & T, you will learn to:
	ensure that the working area is well ordered and safe, and that equipment is well maintained
	use equipment safely; follow safe working practices and understand the procedures for dealing with accidents
	recognise that materials and equipment need to be safely stored and maintained
	be aware of the dangers of the misuse of materials and equipment, and the consequent risk of accidents
	check the condition of equipment before use
	identify hazards in the working environment and to take appropriate action if dangerous situations occur
	recognise that products must be electrically and mechanically safe

How you behave

You should always be sensible. Don't run, shout or fool about, and don't put up with other people fooling about and endangering others. If an accident does happen, make sure that you tell your teacher straight away.

In order to be hygienic, make sure that food preparation surfaces are kept clean and are not used for other purposes. Always wash your hands thoroughly before handling or preparing food. Put all waste food into a covered bin.

Fig. 3.2

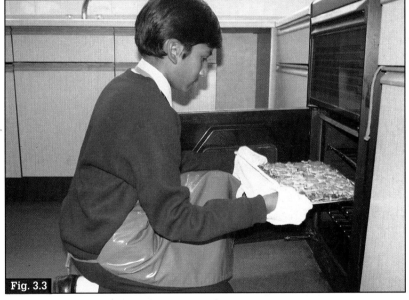

Fig. 3.3

10 Rules for Safe Design & Technology

1. Always ask your teacher's permission before using machinery and electrical equipment.

2. Always use the safety guards on equipment, and eye protection when appropriate.

3. Check the condition of hand tools and tell your teacher about any tools, or knives, that are chipped, blunt or have loose handles.

4. Check the condition of portable electrical appliances like irons and soldering irons. Tell your teacher if anything is wrong with an appliance, such as a frayed flex or a loose screw.

5. Only use chemicals and glues in well-ventilated areas. Never use them near food or on surfaces used for food preparation.

6. Never leave working machinery, or hot pans of fat, unattended.

7. Don't distract people who are operating machinery, or removing hot food from ovens or hobs.

8. Clean all equipment properly when you have finished using it, and report any damage or breakages.

9. Always return tools and equipment to their proper place after use.

10. Leave any hot tools, or hot pieces of work, in a safe place to cool before putting them away. Warn other people about things that are hot.

If you are in any doubt, ask!

This triangular safety symbol appears in this book and in *Design & Technology: The Process* when there is something important that you should know about safety. Make sure that you always take note of what it says.

EXTRAS

1. Would you know what to do in the case of an accident or a fire? Draw a sketch map of your Design & Technology rooms. Then mark on your map all of the following things: the emergency exits; the gangways that must be kept as 'clearways' so that the emergency exits are always accessible; the fire extinguishers (state what type of fire they are for); the emergency stop buttons (state when you should use them); the first aid boxes (state who you should tell if somebody hurts themselves); and the place where you should assemble if there is a fire.

4 CONSTRUCTION MATERIALS

Every day we come into contact with many different materials. Everything constructed by people is made from some type of material.

The development of humans and the materials that they use are closely linked. Historians have named periods of history after the most important material used by people at that time: for example, the Stone Age, the Bronze Age, and the Iron Age.

There are many different types of material in use today. They include wood, metal, plastics, stone, bone, foam, glass, rubber, cotton, wool, paper, card, leather, fur, brick, and clay.

Classifying materials

Materials can be classified (arranged) into two groups. A material is either **natural** or **manufactured** (made by people).

Natural	wood
	clay
	leather
	stone
	fur
	wool

Manufactured	plastic
	metal
	paper
	brick
	card

	In D&T, you will learn to:
	consider, when selecting and using materials, their physical and aesthetic properties, availability and cost, and the product being made
	use factual information and value judgements
	recognise the aesthetic qualities of natural and manufactured materials

Fig. 4.1

Choosing materials

It is important that the materials you use when constructing your design are suitable. Different materials have different properties, which means that they are suitable for different uses. When choosing a material for a specific purpose you need to know what properties and characteristics to look for. You can do this by asking a series of questions about the material:

● How strong does it need to be?

● Does it need to be heavy or light?

● Does it need to be rigid or flexible?

● Does it need to be weatherproof?

● Is the colour important?

● Is it easily available?

● Can I afford to buy it?

● Does it have to be easily shaped?

● Does it need to be environmentally friendly?

● Does it need to be safe for children to use?

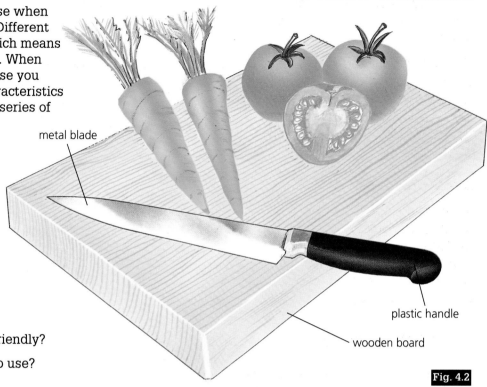

metal blade

plastic handle

wooden board

Fig. 4.2

It is no good choosing a material that it is not suitable as you will only waste time, money and effort on your work. Sometimes it is difficult to choose the correct material, but at other times it is very obvious.

Good choices of material:

● ceramic casserole dish

● rigid, strong, plastic safety helmet

● paper disposable cup

● waterproof fabric for a raincoat

● plastic carrier bag

Poor choices of material:

● wooden casserole dish

● woollen safety helmet

● gold disposable cup

● paper raincoat

● lead carrier bag

The rest of this chapter looks at the construction materials used in schools – paper, card, clay, wood, metal and plastic.

Fig. 4.3

EXTRAS

1. Can you think of any more silly objects made from unsuitable materials?

Sheet Materials

Paper, card and thin plastic sheet are all **sheet materials** (see Fig. 4.4). They are excellent materials for constructing your designs. They can be easily cut and folded to make three-dimensional shapes and forms. Paper and thin card can be cut using scissors, but to cut thicker card and thin plastic you will need to use a modelling knife. You should always protect the table or bench top by using a cutting board under your work. Special cutting mats are available (see Fig. 4.5) but a thick piece of scrap card or board will also work. When cutting with a knife, never use a plastic ruler as a straight edge. Always use a special metal safety ruler which will help to protect your fingers if the knife slips (see Fig. 4.6).

Safety

Safety is very important when working with sharp tools. Never run around with knives or scissors in your hand or in a pocket. Whenever possible, cover or retract the knife blade when you are not using it.

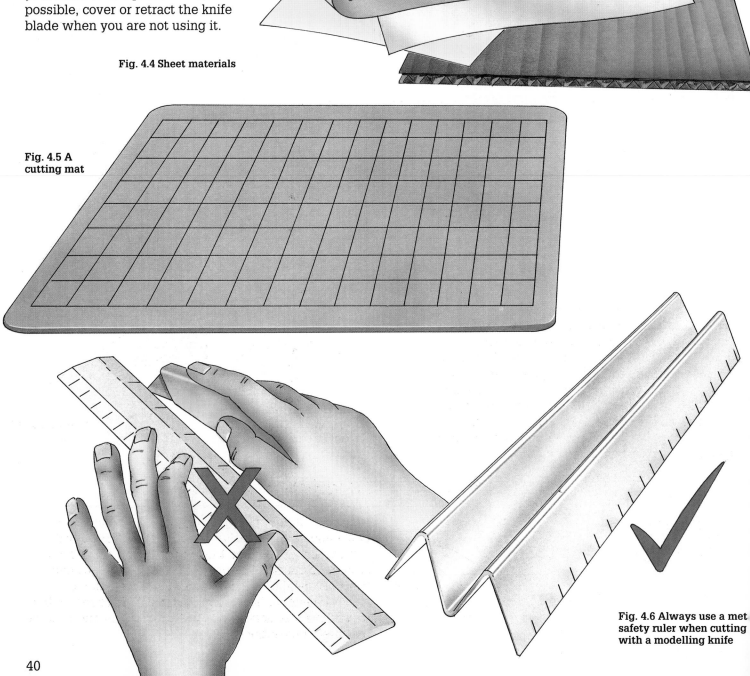

Fig. 4.4 Sheet materials

Fig. 4.5 A cutting mat

Fig. 4.6 Always use a met safety ruler when cutting with a modelling knife

Nets

A flat shape which can be folded or bent to produce a three-dimensional shape is known as a development or a **net**. Fig 4.7 shows the net for making three-dimensional cylinders, cones and cubes. When designing nets it is important to remember to include tabs or flaps in your design. They will be needed to enable you to glue your model together.

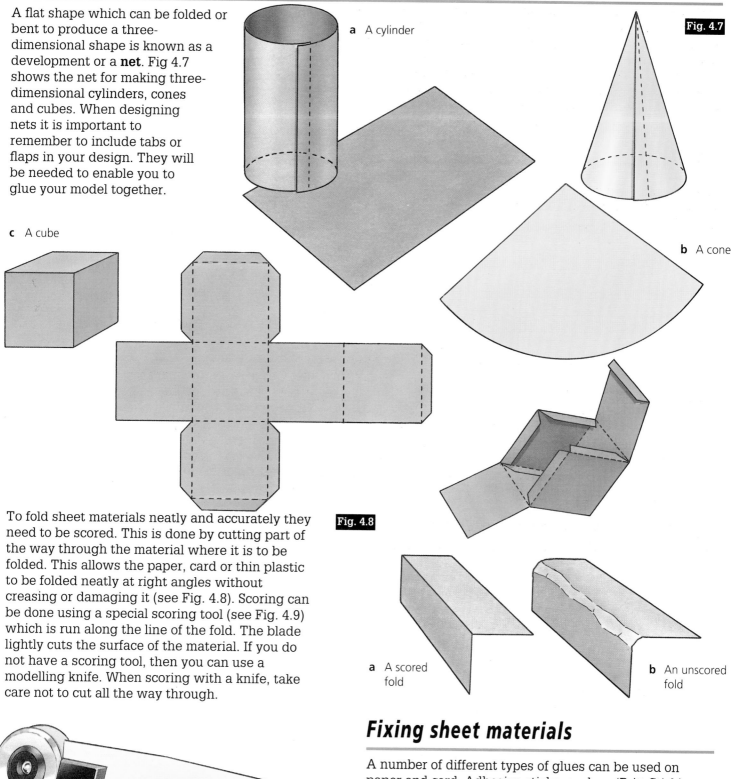

a A cylinder

Fig. 4.7

b A cone

c A cube

Fig. 4.8

To fold sheet materials neatly and accurately they need to be scored. This is done by cutting part of the way through the material where it is to be folded. This allows the paper, card or thin plastic to be folded neatly at right angles without creasing or damaging it (see Fig. 4.8). Scoring can be done using a special scoring tool (see Fig. 4.9) which is run along the line of the fold. The blade lightly cuts the surface of the material. If you do not have a scoring tool, then you can use a modelling knife. When scoring with a knife, take care not to cut all the way through.

a A scored fold

b An unscored fold

Fig. 4.9 A scoring tool

Fixing sheet materials

A number of different types of glues can be used on paper and card. Adhesive sticks, such as 'Pritt Stick', work well on paper and thin card, but you may need a stronger contact adhesive for thick card. Plastic sheet materials can be joined together with either special plastic cement or hot melt glue guns. Always remember to read the instructions on the glue carefully and observe the safety precautions.

Constructions using Sheet Materials

When using paper, card or thin plastic as a construction material, it will often have to support loads and forces. To do this it will need to be strengthened.

Folded sheet materials

The simplest way to strengthen a piece of paper is to fold it. You can try this yourself by taking a piece of A4 drawing paper and folding it down the middle. Compare this with a sheet of unfolded A4 paper. The folded sheet is more rigid than the unfolded one. Fig. 4.10 shows paper folded in several different ways. Which one do you think is the strongest? Corrugated card and plastic make use of this principle – they provide strong, lightweight construction materials.

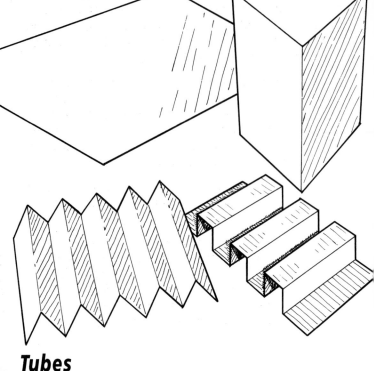

Fig. 4.10 A sheet of paper made stronger by folding

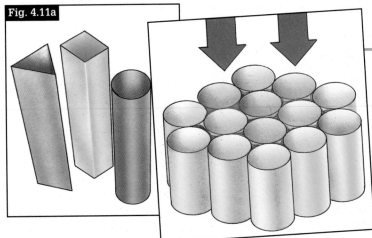

Fig. 4.11a

Tubes

Another way of strengthening sheet materials is to make them into tubes. Tubes can be strong, and when used together can support heavy loads. You can try this out for yourself by collecting the cardboard tubes from the centres of toilet or kitchen rolls, and sticking them together with adhesive tape. Stand them on their ends and load them with weights. The results may surprise you.

Fig. 4.11b Tubes are very strong when used together, standing on their ends

Frames

Simple frame structures can be made using small triangles of card and strips of wood. Joining strips of wood by simply sticking them together with glue is called **butt jointing**. A butt joint relies only on the glue for its strength and really needs to be strengthened. Card can be used to reinforce the joint and the corners to make a much stronger structure (see Fig. 4.12).

You may have noticed in the drawings on this page that triangles are used a great deal to strengthen materials. For example, triangular folded paper is stronger than rectangular folded paper (see Fig. 4.10); the supports on the butt joint and corner are also triangular (see Fig. 4.12). A square or rectangular frame can be pushed over, but a triangular frame is rigid. (For more information about triangulation see page 156.)

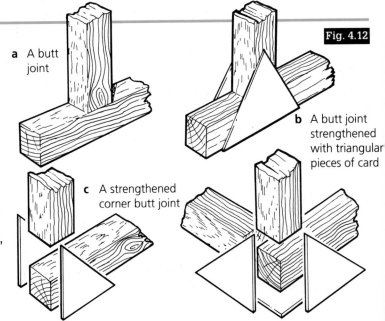

Fig. 4.12

a A butt joint

b A butt joint strengthened with triangular pieces of card

c A strengthened corner butt joint

Clay

Clay is an important natural material. It is formed from earth and minerals by the effects of the weather over a period of thousands of years. When clay is wet, it behaves like soft plastic and can be moulded and shaped, but once it has dried, it becomes hard and leathery.

People have used clay to make pots since earliest times. At first they were just left to dry naturally. These pots were easily broken, however. It was then discovered that if the dry pots were put into a very hot fire they became permanently hard. These pots were now stronger and much less brittle.

Clay is still an important material today, and is used in a variety of different industries, including brick and tile making, engineering and paper making.

Fired clay objects are called **ceramics**. There are different types of ceramic materials, with different weights, strengths and colours. For example, cups and saucers are made of lightweight porcelain or bone china whereas casserole dishes, which need to withstand high temperatures, are often made from stoneware which is heavier and stronger.

Fig. 4.13 Using clay to make bricks in India

Wedging

Before clay can be used to make pots, any air inside it has to be removed. If pockets of air become trapped inside the clay the work will crack during the drying out or firing stage. The process of removing air from the clay is called **wedging**, and is done by banging it on to a firm surface such as a table or bench (see Fig. 4.14). The aim is to bang the clay so hard that it drives the air out of it. Wedging can also be done by smacking or slapping the clay with the palms of your hands. However, you should take care not to punch it with your knuckles or fingers as this will only make holes or pockets which will trap more air. You can check to see if any air is trapped inside the clay by cutting it with a wire cutter (see Fig. 4.15). If the inside of the block of clay is free from air holes then it is ready for use.

Fig. 4.14 Wedging clay on a strong bench

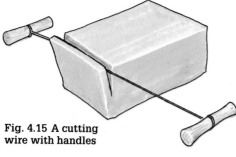

Fig. 4.15 A cutting wire with handles

EXTRAS

1. Look at a book on origami. Find and follow the instructions for making a paper structure, such as a box to contain a product.

2. Find out which types of ceramic crockery can be placed in a microwave oven, and which types should not be put in a dishwasher.

Pinch pots

One of the simplest (and probably the oldest) method of using clay is to make pinch pots. A ball of clay is held in one hand while the thumb of the other hand is pressed into it. By pinching the thumb and fingers together while turning the clay with the other hand, a simple pot can be formed (see Fig. 4.16). The pinching technique can also be used to make hollow models out of clay. The clay can be shaped by squeezing and pinching until you have the shape you want.

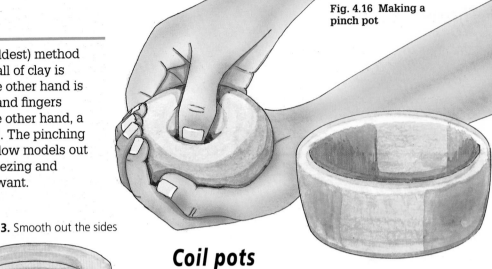
Fig. 4.16 Making a pinch pot

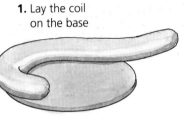
1. Lay the coil on the base

2. Build up the coils

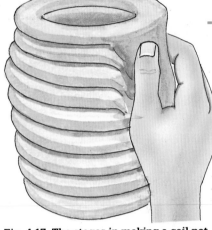
3. Smooth out the sides

Fig. 4.17 The stages in making a coil pot

Coil pots

Clay can be rolled out into long coils which are then used to make pots. First, a piece of clay is flattened out and cut to make a base for the pot. Then a clay coil is placed around the edge of the base, rather like coiling rope. The pot is then built up by adding more coils of clay. When all the coils have been added, the clay inside the pot is smoothed out with the fingers to cover the joins between the coils, forming a continuous surface. This helps to make it stronger and prevents it from coming apart during drying. The outside of the pot can either be left showing the coils or it too can be smoothed out (see Fig. 4.17).

Slab pots

Clay can be rolled out between a rolling pin and two guide sticks to form tiles or slabs (see Fig. 4.18). The slabs can then be shaped over plaster moulds to form bowls or plates, or they can be used flat and joined together to form boxes. Pottery made in this way is generally known as slabware (see Fig. 4.19).

If you intend to build pots from slabs you should roll out the slabs and let them dry a little before trying to stick them together. The clay can be handled much more easily if it has been allowed to become **leather hard** (i.e. not floppy, but before it reaches the bone dry stage). The slabs are then 'glued' together by scoring the edges to be joined and spreading over them a paste of wet clay known as **slip**. Then the joints are smoothed and sealed with slip before the pot is set aside to dry before firing.

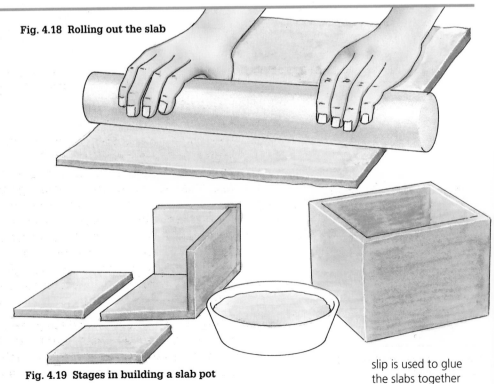
Fig. 4.18 Rolling out the slab

Fig. 4.19 Stages in building a slab pot

slip is used to glue the slabs together

Throwing a pot

Making pots on a potter's wheel is known as **throwing** and requires a lot of skill and practice to do well (see Fig. 4.20). Some potter's wheels are operated by kicking or pushing a bar connected to the wheel. These are known as kick wheels. You may have wheels in your school which are driven by an electric motor, the speed of which is controlled by pushing down a pedal.

Before throwing a pot, the clay needs to be prepared properly. It needs to be smoothed and formed into a ball. If you are making a set of bowls, for example, you must make sure each ball of clay is the same weight. This should mean that the finished bowls are all the same size.

The first stage in throwing is to centre the piece of clay on the wheel. A ball of clay is pressed on to the centre of the wheel and sprinkled with water to lubricate it. The wheel is turned and the clay pressed with both hands until it spins smoothly in the centre of the wheel without wobbling or showing signs of being off centre. Then, while it is spinning, the hands are used to mould the clay into the shape required.

Fig. 4.20 When throwing a pot it is a good idea to wear an apron

Biscuit firing

Once your work is complete, it can be set aside to dry. Clay is best allowed to dry slowly and evenly. If it is dried too quickly it can distort or crack. Once dry, it can be placed in a large oven called a **kiln** and heated to between 1000°–1150°C to remove any remaining moisture, and to let the minerals in the clay fuse together. This is called **biscuit firing** and the pot is now referred to as biscuit clay. Before firing, clay pots can be recycled by simply putting them into water – the clay can then be used again. After firing, it becomes a hard ceramic material which can no longer be re-shaped or recycled.

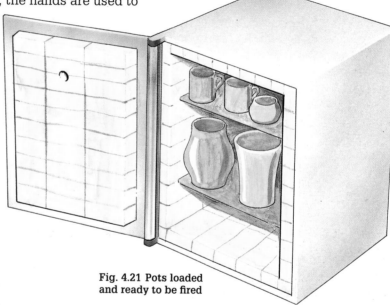

Fig. 4.21 Pots loaded and ready to be fired

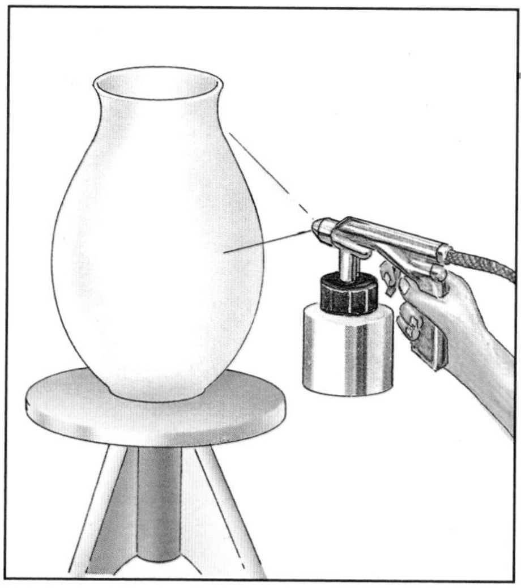

Glazing

After the biscuit firing, pots often have a rough surface which soaks up water. They can be sealed and decorated by applying a glass-like substance called **glaze**. Glazes contain things such as feldspar, china clay, borax and lead. They are mixed together and ground down to a fine powder. Water is added, and a creamy mixture is made which is applied to the pots. Glaze is put on to the pots by dipping them into it, spraying or brushing it on (see Fig. 4.22). When fired to a high temperature, glaze becomes glossy and does not let water through. The colour and clearness of the glaze depends upon the chemicals or oxides used in the glaze itself. For example, cobalt gives a blue glaze, copper gives a green glaze and manganese gives a purplish-brown glaze.

Always take care when handling glazes. They may contain chemicals which can be harmful, so always wash your hands thoroughly afterwards. Use a mask to prevent you from breathing in the dust when mixing or spraying glazes – some chemicals and minerals are dangerous to your lungs.

Fig. 4.22 Glazes can be applied by spraying the pot

Woods

Wood is a natural material that has been used for many centuries by builders and craftspeople. Until recently it has been easily available and there has been a seemingly endless supply. However, it takes trees at least 30 years (and some over 100 years) to mature and produce wood suitable for human use. If trees are cut down at a faster rate than they are planted, soon there will be little wood to use. The clearing of rain forests is an example of this kind of destruction.

The grain

Trees grow by producing cells which are long and thin. This becomes the 'wood'. We call the pattern of the cells the **grain**. It is the grain that gives the different types of wood their distinctive appearance. Look at Fig. 4.23. The magnified views show the grain in detail.

The way that the grain is fastened together gives a clue to the fact that wood is stronger in one direction than the other. This is important. Wood is always cut with the grain in the long direction of the plank (see Fig. 4.24).

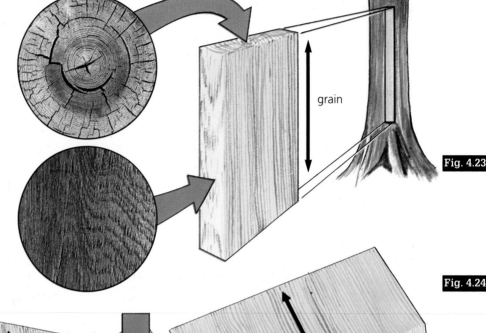

grain

Fig. 4.23

Fig. 4.24

grain

grain

breaks easily

grain

very strong

Softwoods

Softwoods come mainly from fast-growing trees, such as pine. They have needle-like leaves, like Christmas trees. The wood is used extensively in buildings for roofs, door frames, floor supports and window frames. These woods are low in cost and easy to work with. As they grow quickly they can be grown as a crop and easily replaced.

In D&T, you will learn to:
recognise that materials have different working properties
use knowledge and understanding of materials to design and make structures which stand up to stress

Hardwoods

Hardwoods come from slower growing trees such as oak, ash and mahogany. They can take up to 100 years to grow and are expensive to buy. They are generally harder and stronger than softwoods. Hardwoods are often used for making furniture and for decorative purposes. Sometimes thin slices (veneers) of hardwood are fixed on top of cheaper woods, especially plywood. This allows furniture-makers to use the valuable hardwood as decoration without destroying so many trees.

Plywood

Plywood is made from thin slices of wood glued together under pressure. The grain of each layer is placed at right angles to the grain of the layer before (see Fig. 4.25). This increases the strength of the material and gives plywood its distinctive striped edge. It is used where large flat surfaces are required. White plywood is usually made from birch. Red plywood is made from tropical timbers, often mahogany. By using waterproof glues, red plywood can be made waterproof enough for use outdoors.

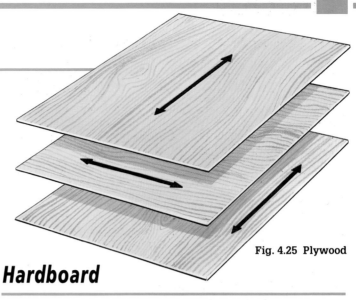

Fig. 4.25 Plywood

Chipboard

Chipboard is made by compressing chips and shavings of wood and gluing them together. This is a cheap way of producing usable boards from waste timber. Chipboard is often used to make floors in buildings. When it is covered in a veneer of wood or a printed paper, it can be used to make flat-sided furniture, such as cupboards and wardrobes.

Hardboard

Hardboard is a dark brown material produced in large, thin sheets from compressed and glued wood, rags and waste materials. It is smooth on one side only. Hardboard can be pre-covered in a coloured, or a timber-like paper finish, which increases its usual low cost.

Fig 4.26 Commonly used woods

Material	Colour	Weight	Strength	Weatherproof	Cost	Uses
Pine (softwood)	Yellowish-white	Light	Medium	If treated	Medium	General construction work
Redwood (softwood)	Pale yellow	Light	Medium	If treated	Medium	General construction work; out door use if preserved
Oak (hardwood)	Light brown	Heavy	High	Good	High	Quality furniture; often used in churches because of its durability
Mahogany (hardwood)	Reddish	Medium	High	Good	High	Quality furniture
Teak (hardwood)	Dark brown	Heavy	High	Very good	Very high	High quality boats and furniture
Beech (hardwood)	Pale brown	Heavy	High	Good	High	Work benches, tool handles
Plywood (manufactured)	White or red	Medium	High	Good	Medium	Toys, drawer bottoms, boats
Chipboard (manufactured)	Pale chips of wood	High	Medium	Poor	Low	Flat-pack furniture, kitchen units
Hardboard (manufactured)	Dark brown	Medium	Low	Poor	Very low	Cupboard backs

EXTRAS

1. Collect together different types of wood. Look at them under a magnifying glass. Can you see the different sized cells that grew slowly in the winter? Try to identify them as softwoods or hardwoods.

Metals

Metals are made from inorganic ores that have been mined from the earth and then smelted (heated until the ore melts) so that the metal can be extracted. Metals are generally very tough and durable. They can be bent, especially when very hot. A blacksmith shapes iron when it is red hot.

When metals are melted they can be poured into shaped moulds. This is called **casting** and is used to make a metal vice, for example. Metals are very versatile materials. They can be stamped with a pattern, as with coins, made into thin sheets, pressed and painted, as with a car body. Metals can be joined and sealed as in containers for food and drinks. They can be very strong yet light, as in aircraft, or used for delicate decoration as, for example, when making jewellery. Metals can also conduct electricity and heat.

Fig. 4.27 An iron works

Steel

The most commonly used metal is **steel**. It is used, for instance, in the construction of bridges, cars and ships. Steel is made by refining iron and adding small amounts of carbon to give it greater strength. Ordinary steel will rust if exposed to the weather. If it is not painted it will become weak and flake away. Adding nickel to steel prevents it from rusting; it is then called **stainless steel**. This is the kind used for kitchenware and cutlery.

Aluminium

Aluminum is the next most commonly used metal, after steel. It is light and strong but more expensive to produce than steel. Ordinary aluminum is used in the production of kitchen pans and soft drinks containers. The aircraft industry uses a special type of aluminium called **duraluminium**, which is very strong, but very expensive to produce.

Zinc and tin

Zinc and **tin** are metals that are used to coat steel to make it weatherproof. When steel is coated with zinc it is called **galvanised steel** which is used for making dustbins and wheelbarrows. Steel coated with tin is called **tin plate**, and is used in the food canning business.

	In D&T, you will learn to:
	recognise that materials have different working properties
	know the working properties of a range of materials

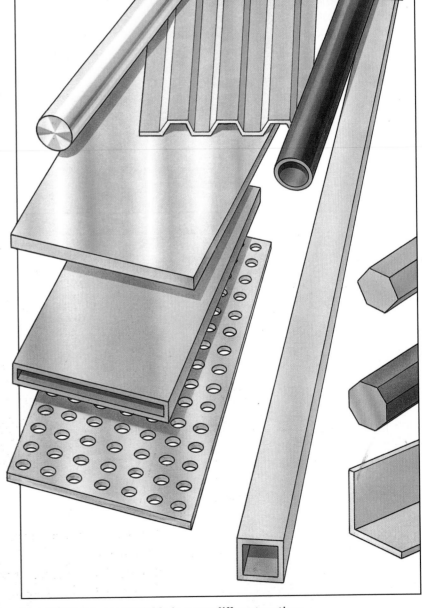

Fig. 4.28 Metals are available in many different sections

Fig. 4.29 Metals commonly used

Material	Colour	Weight	Strength	Weatherproof	Cost	Uses
Mild steel	Grey	High	High	Poor	Low	Building construction, bridges, cars, pylons
Stainless steel	Grey	High	High	High	High	Cutlery, pans, boat fittings
Aluminium	Grey	Low	High	High	Medium	Pans, kitchen foil, window frames, greenhouse frames, drinks cans
Copper	Pink	High	Medium	High	High	Electrical wires, saucepans
Tin plate	Grey/White	Medium	High	High	Medium	Food containers (tins)
Brass	Yellow	High	Medium	High	High	Boat fittings, taps, ornaments

Fig. 4.30

EXTRAS

1. Look at the pictures on this page and decide what metals have been used.

2. Look in the kitchen at home. What objects made from metal can you find? Make a list of them.

Plastics

Plastics are relatively new materials, made mostly from oil. The word 'plastic' means easily shaped. There are several different kinds of plastic. Their correct names are not easy to remember, for example, polyvynilchloride, polypropylene and polymethylmethacrylate. However, many of these plastics have been given names which are much easier to remember, for example, polyvynilchloride is more commonly known as **PVC**.

Plastics can be made to be almost any type of material that is required. They can be soft or hard, light or heavy, strong or weak. They are made by a chemical 'cooking' process. The ingredients are simple, but the number of different outcomes is almost limitless.

There are two families of plastics – **thermosetting plastics** (including resins) and **thermoplastics**.

Thermosetting plastics

Thermosetting plastics will melt the first time they are heated. However, when cooled the plastic (as its name suggests) sets, and remains hard even if it is reheated. Thermosetting plastics are usually made into artefacts by heating powder in a mould. They are used to make such things as electric plugs and sockets, light switches and kitchen spoons. These plastics are not often used in school technology.

Resins

Resins are used as liquids. When they are mixed with a hardener they will set in a few minutes. Resins can be strengthened by including strands of glass, making **GRP** (glass-reinforced plastic). This is used to make very strong, complex shell shapes, such as racing car bodies and baths. Resins can also be used as glues to fix glass and metals that normal glues will not bond.

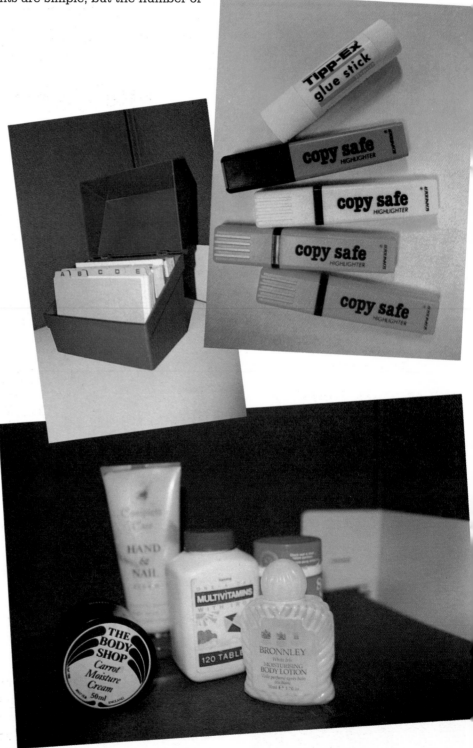

In D&T, you will learn to:
recognise that materials have different working properties
recognise the aesthetic qualities of natural and manufactured materials
know the working properties of a range of materials

Fig. 4.31

Thermoplastics

Thermoplastics can be softened by heating. They set again when cooled. The material will soften and harden as often as required. This allows the plastic to be bent, twisted and stretched easily. If heated further, thermoplastics can be squeezed out into shapes, like squeezing toothpaste out of a tube. This is called **extrusion**. They can also be shaped by heating and then blown, like bubble gum. If thermoplastic is blown into shaped holes, it produces bottles. Thermoplastics are good insulators of electricity, so they are used to cover electrical cables.

They are also good heat insulators, and are used for pan handles, for example.

The use of plastics for containers, from plastic bags to shaped chocolate boxes, has become very common today. Plastics do create problems, however. They don't rot very easily – they are **non bio-degradable**. Some plastics can be recycled and used again. As most plastics are made from oil, of which there is not much left, recycling is becoming increasingly necessary.

Acrylic

Acrylic is the most common plastic used in school technology. Its chemical name is polymethylmethacrylate but most people just call it acrylic. It is available in many different colours as sheets or as round rods. Acrylic is an attractive material and it can resist the weather very well. These properties make it ideal for signs outside shops (see Fig. 4.32). It can be softened and bent, blown or twisted to many different shapes. When clear, it can be used as windows and is much stronger than glass, although it will scratch fairly easily. It is used in aircraft windows because it is so tough.

Fig. 4.32

Polystyrene foam

Polystyrene foam can be easily shaped and is very light. This makes it suitable for modelling a three-dimensional object (see Fig. 4.34). For example, modelling a telephone handset using this material is simple and effective.

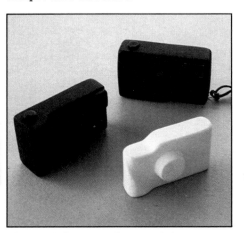

Fig. 4.34 Polystyrene foam models

Fig. 4.33 Computer games made of acrylic

EXTRAS

1. A visit to a local shopping centre can reveal many different containers. Make a list of all the plastic containers that you can find. Have any of them got special features?

2. Collect a range of plastic articles and try to identify them as either thermosetting or thermoplastic materials.

Marking Out

When materials are to be cut to shape they should be marked out first. This means that lines are placed on the surface of the material to show where the cuts are to be made. The different surfaces of metal, wood, card and plastic require different marking tools.

MAKING THE MARKS

Paper and card

A pencil is the best tool to use on paper and card. A pencil with a soft lead ('B' pencil) allows you to correct your mistakes by rubbing out your lines. A hard pencil ('H' pencil) produces a crisp, thin line but will not be as easy to rub out.

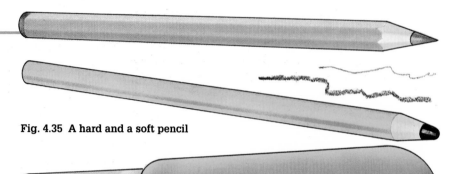

Fig. 4.35 A hard and a soft pencil

Wood

When marking out wood you can use a pencil or a marking knife. A pencil allows you to draw curved shapes which is especially useful when using plywood. With a marking knife you can make a clear, thin cut across the grain.

Fig. 4.36 A marking knife

Plastic

Plastic requires a spirit-based marker pen. These pens come in different thicknesses. You should use a thin one for greatest accuracy. The lines can be removed by cleaning the plastic with solvent. You could also use a chinagraph pencil to mark out plastic.

Fig. 4.37 A spirit-based marker pen

Metal

Marks are usually made on metal with a scriber. If the metal is first coated with marking blue (a blue die), the marks show up much better. A spirit-based marker pen is often used on sheet aluminium. Deep marks must be polished away.

Clay

When clay is soft, a sharp tool can make marks easily. When it is drying, prior to firing, a scriber is the most suitable marking tool.

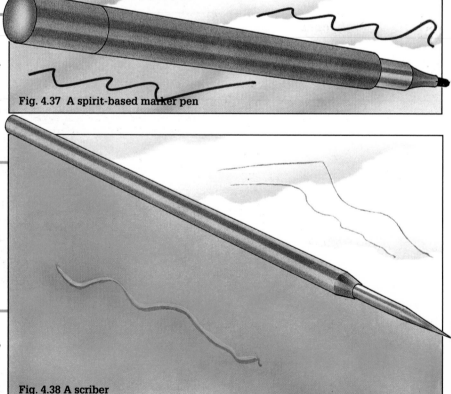

Fig. 4.38 A scriber

	In D&T, you will learn to:
	recognise the appropriate tools for working with a variety of materials
	select and use equipment correctly
	test simple objects to determine performance

Collect a range of materials and a range of marking tools. Devise a series of test to test the effectiveness of different marking tools. Can the marks be removed easily? Can the lines be drawn easily? How clear are the lines?

GUIDING THE MARKS

To produce straight, curved or odd-shaped lines you may need special tools to guide the pen, pencil or other marking tool.

Straight lines

To draw straight lines you will need to use different tools to guide you. For lines parallel to an edge you should use either a marking gauge for wood (see Fig. 4.39a) or a pair of odd-leg calipers for metal (see Fig. 4.39b). Lines at right angles to an edge can be easily drawn using a try square (see Fig. 4.39c). A rule or straight edge can be used for other straight lines (see Fig. 4.39d).

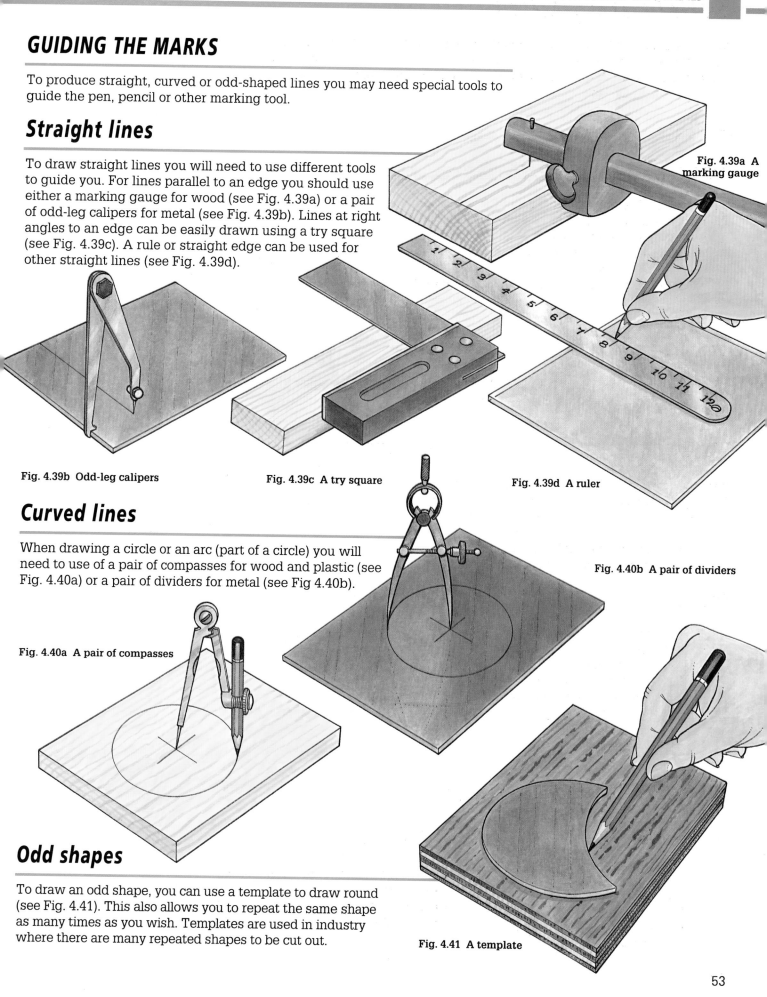

Fig. 4.39a A marking gauge

Fig. 4.39b Odd-leg calipers

Fig. 4.39c A try square

Fig. 4.39d A ruler

Curved lines

When drawing a circle or an arc (part of a circle) you will need to use of a pair of compasses for wood and plastic (see Fig. 4.40a) or a pair of dividers for metal (see Fig 4.40b).

Fig. 4.40b A pair of dividers

Fig. 4.40a A pair of compasses

Odd shapes

To draw an odd shape, you can use a template to draw round (see Fig. 4.41). This also allows you to repeat the same shape as many times as you wish. Templates are used in industry where there are many repeated shapes to be cut out.

Fig. 4.41 A template

Saws and Sawing

Having marked out your material you will now need to shape it. Saws are used to remove large pieces of unwanted material quickly. There are many different types of saws, and you must be able to select from a few basic saws the one that will do the job required. This choice of tool is crucial if you are to work in a safe, efficient and accurate way.

Machine saws

Jigsaws are used to saw wood and plastic. They have a small blade that is moved up and down rapidly by an electric motor (see Fig. 4.42). The blade does not move far in either direction. The work to be cut is held firmly by hand on a flat cutting table. The work is then gently pressed against the moving blade. Curves can be cut by rotating the work as it reaches the blade. These saws, as with all machines in a workshop, should only be used with the permission of your teacher. If there is a guard fitted, it must be used.

Fig. 4.42 A machine jigsaw

Saws for wood

Tenon saws are used to cut pieces of wood to the right length. They are also used to saw straight lines when cutting joints. The wide blade does not allow you to cut curves. The blade is stiffened with a strip of metal along the top of the blade to stop it bending when you saw (see Fig. 4.43). You should always hold the wood being cut in a vice or use a bench hook (see Fig. 4.44).

Fig. 4.43 A tenon saw

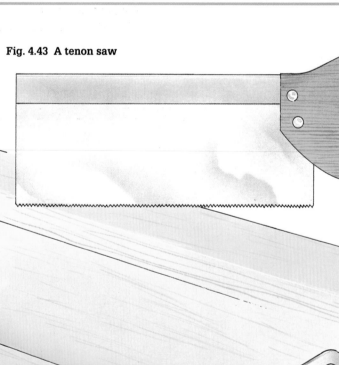

Fig. 4.44 Using a tenon saw with a bench hook

	In D&T, you will learn to:
	take account of the constraints imposed by equipment
	identify and use machines to perform tasks required by your design activities
	recognise that materials have different working properties

Coping saws have thin blades, allowing you to make a curved cut. It is nearly impossible to cut a straight line with a coping saw, so use it only for curves. The blade is held in tension in a frame which allows you to twist the blade to cut in different directions (see Fig. 4.45).

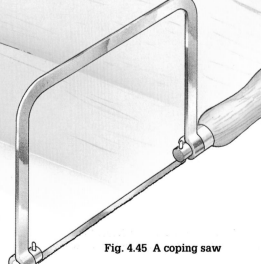

Fig. 4.45 A coping saw

Saws for metal

Hacksaws have replaceable blades that are held tightly in a frame (see Fig. 4.46). The blade is about 30 cm long and you can cut straight lines with it. When using a hacksaw, the teeth on the blade should point away from the handle to cut well.

The **junior hacksaw** is a small version of the hacksaw with a shorter blade which has much smaller teeth (see Fig. 4.47). This saw is used to cut small, thin pieces of metal. Do not use it to cut thick pieces of metal – it will take far too long because the small teeth cut slowly, and the blade may break.

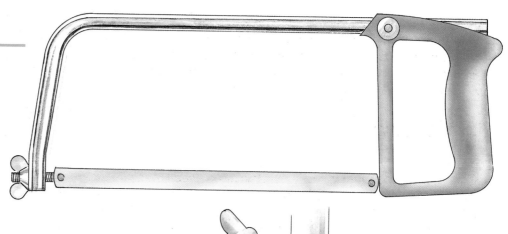

Fig. 4.46 A hacksaw has adjustable blades

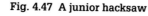

Fig. 4.47 A junior hacksaw

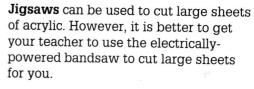

Saws for acrylic

Jigsaws can be used to cut large sheets of acrylic. However, it is better to get your teacher to use the electrically-powered bandsaw to cut large sheets for you.

Coping saws are used to cut acrylic in the same way as they are used to saw wood. The sheet acrylic must be held securely in a vice close to the sawing point. If you allow the acrylic to flex whilst cutting it will probably break, so take care and cut gently. Work at a gentle, slowish pace because too much friction will cause heat that may melt the acrylic and result in the blade getting stuck.

Hacksaws are best used on metal (see above) but they can be used to cut acrylic. The only problem when using a hacksaw is that you must hold the acrylic very securely to prevent it from flexing and snapping.

All saws cut wood. Fingers are softer than wood, so take great care when using any saw.

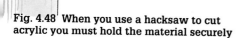

Fig. 4.48 When you use a hacksaw to cut acrylic you must hold the material securely

Shaping Materials

Once the large areas of waste material are removed by sawing, the final shaping can take place. Shaping tools remove only small amounts of material. Skill is required to produce a good and true surface – and you will need to practice with these tools before you are able to use them accurately.

Planes

Planes are mostly used on wood. They have sharp blades that cut a thin shaving off when you push them across the surface of the wood. The wood must be held firmly in a vice, whilst you use the plane. Hold the plane in both hands and push along the length of the grain, changing direction if a rough surface is left (see Fig. 4.49).

The plane can be used to plane the end of a piece of wood but the wood tends to split, so care must be taken. To prevent the splitting, work from both ends towards the middle, not right across the end.

Planes can also be used on acrylic. Planing the edge of an acrylic sheet produces a smooth surface but the plane requires frequent sharpening as acrylic blunts the plane blade quickly.

Fig. 4.49 A plane

Fig. 4.50 Using a file on acrylic

In D&T, you will learn to:
take account of the constraints imposed by equipment
recognise the appropriate tools for working with a variety of materials
understand that it may be necessary to practise an operation in order to improve quality

Files

Files are used on both metal and plastic. Different shaped files are available to cut different shaped surfaces (see Fig. 4.51). Files also vary in the size of their teeth – the smaller the teeth, the smoother and finer the surface produced. Whatever their size, the teeth need frequent cleaning to prevent them from becoming clogged. If you rub chalk on to the file before using it, you can help prevent the file from clogging.

Files must always be used with a correctly fitted handle. Using a file without a handle is dangerous.

Fig. 4.51 Different shapes of files

Fig. 4.52 A rasp

Rasps

A **rasp** is a file designed to be used on wood (see Fig. 4.52). The teeth are bigger and will cut quickly. If used on hard metal, a rasp will not cut and it will become blunt. A rasp produces a very rough surface and therefore should only be used for quick approximate shaping. After using a rasp, further work (such as sanding down the surface with glass paper) must be done to make the wood smooth.

Surforms

Surforms are special file-like tools with replaceable blades (see Fig. 4.53). They are used on wood and thick pieces of acrylic. They can be flat or round in shape. Surforms cut quickly, but they tend to splinter the edges of the wood, so take care.

Fig. 4.53 A surform has replaceable blades

Tin snips

Tin snips (shears) are used in exactly the same way as a pair of scissors. They will cut thick card or thin metal. When thin metal is cut it always has a sharp edge. This edge must be smoothed with a file to round the corners slightly, which will reduce the danger of cuts. When cutting with tin snips, take care of your fingers.

Fig. 4.54 Tin snips can be held in a vice to make it easier to cut thin metal

Chisels

Chisels are used to remove wood waste only, and they should **not** be used on acrylic. The blade on a chisel, which must be kept sharp, is exposed and dangerous. Chisels should therefore be carried carefully, with the blade pointing at the floor. Safety is also very important in the use of chisels. You will have to practise the technique which your teacher will show you, so that you use a chisel safely.

Here are some general rules when using a chisel:

● Always make sure your work is firmly held in a vice.

● Keep both of your hands behind the cutting blade.

● Use the correct size of chisel – the widest possible is a general rule.

● Cut across the grain where possible.

● Hit the chisel with a mallet – *never* use a hammer.

Fig. 4.55 Chiselling a groove across a piece of wood

Fig. 4.56 Chiselling a corner of wood to shape it

Making Holes

You will need to produce many small holes when assembling pieces of wood, metal and plastic. They are all produced in a similar manner. A **hand drill** (wheelbrace) with twist drill can be used for small holes. Different twist drill bits produce different sized holes.

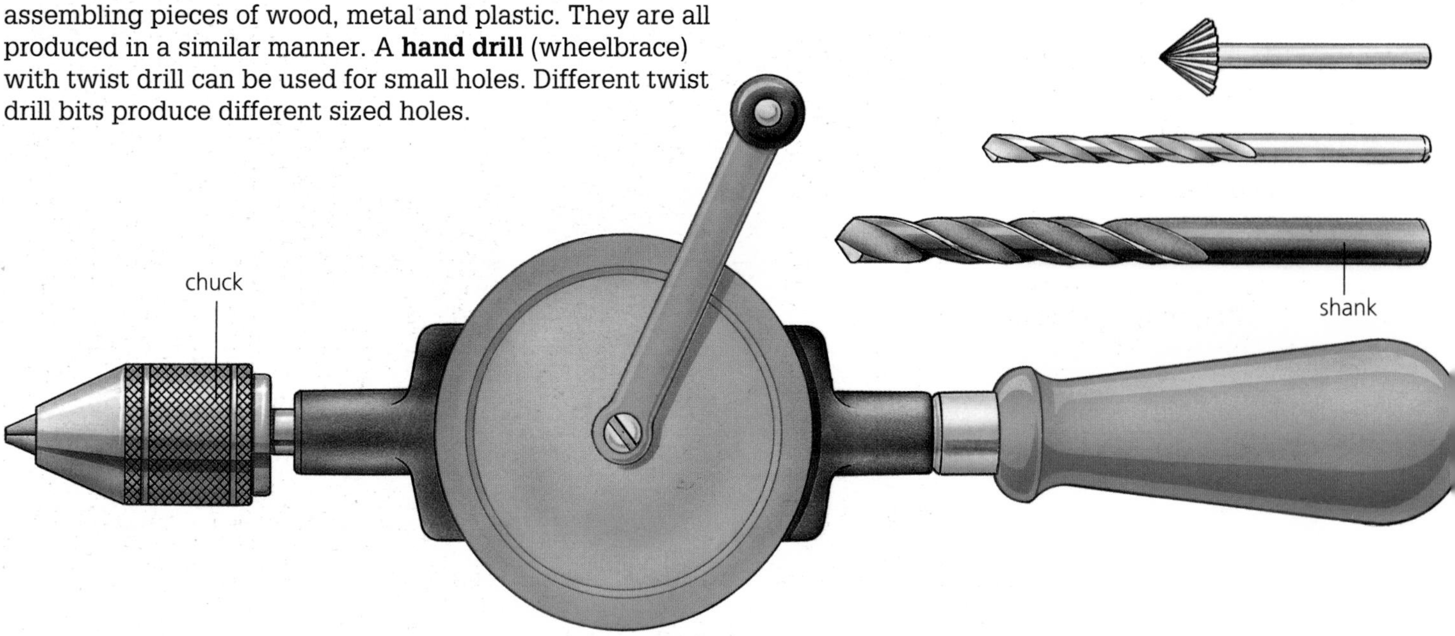

Fig. 4.57 A hand drill

chuck

shank

Small holes

When making small holes you should use a vice or a clamp to make the material secure. To prevent thin acrylic sheets from splitting, a piece of scrap wood should be placed beneath your work.

Drilling by hand

To make correctly positioned and accurate holes you must take care. Hold the drill firmly and at right angles to your work. Press firmly but not too hard, and turn the handle slowly, speeding up when the hole is started.

Fig. 4.58 A left-handed pupil using a hand drill

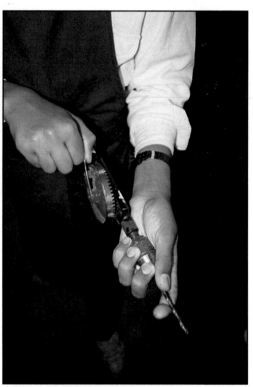

Fig. 4.59 Changing the twist drill

In D&T, you will learn to:	
identify and use machines to perform tasks required by your design activities	
recognise the purpose of equipment, to understand the way it works, and to use it	

Countersunk holes

These are sloping sided holes that will take and hide the shaped head of a screw. These are made by using a countersink drill bit rather than a twist drill bit in your hand drill. Countersink drill bits can be used on wood, plastic or metal.

Fig. 4.60 A countersunk hole

Drilling by machine

Small holes can be drilled with the same twist drill bit used in hand drills, held and turned by a drilling machine. The work must be held securely, and special safety precautions must be observed. Your teacher will demonstrate the safe use of this tool. It must not be used without correct training or without your teacher's permission.

Fig. 4.61 Using a drilling machine

Large holes

A **carpenter's brace** is used to drill large holes in wood. Drill bits with square shanks (ends) are used. The square shank makes it impossible for the bit to slip in the chuck during drilling. Drilling a hole without splitting the wood requires you to drill from both sides of the wood. First drill until the point shows on the other side of the wood (see Fig. 4.62), then turn it round and drill back into the hole using the small hole as a guide.

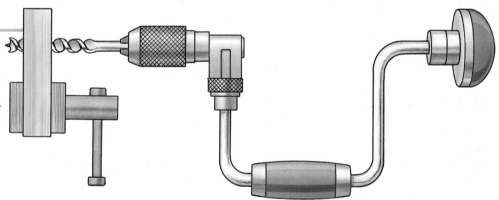

Fig. 4.62 A carpenter's brace

Fig. 4.63 A drill bit

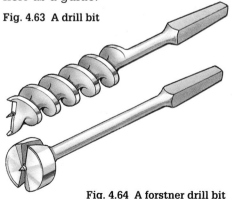

A **forstner drill bit** is a special drill bit with a round shank that is used in the drill machine (see Fig. 4.64). The work must be clamped to the drilling table very securely. These drills give smooth-sided, flat-bottomed holes in wood.

EXTRAS

1. Look at Fig 4.61. Make a list of the safety precautions being taken and the safety features on a drilling machine. Make another list of all the checks you must carry out before using a drilling machine.

Fig. 4.64 A forstner drill bit

Fastenings

Nailing is the quickest way of making a permanent joint in wood. Nails are metal pins, usually made of steel, that are hammered into and through pieces of wood or wood board. When nailing, you should always nail through the thin piece into the thick piece of wood. The strength of nailed joints can be improved by using glue or by sloping the nails, which is called **dovetail nailing** (see Fig. 4.65). The angle of the nail makes it harder to pull the joint apart. Joints can also be strengthened by using glue as well as nails.

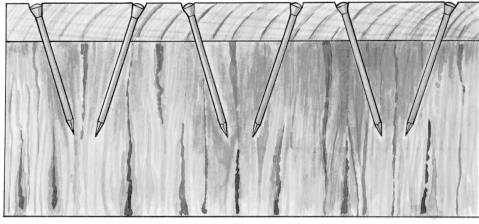

Fig. 4.65 Dovetail nailing

Types of nails

Panel pins are small nails used to fix thin ply and hardboard to a frame. They have small heads that are easily hidden (see Fig. 4.66). **Oval nails** are used where a heavier piece of wood is to be fastened (see Fig 4.67). The oval shape should line up with the grain, rather than across it. Using a **nail punch**, these nails can be driven below the surface so they do not show (see Fig. 4.69). Filling in with a filler and painting will cover all traces of these nails. Oval nails are used in household joinery work. **Round nails** have a large, flat, round head (see Fig. 4.68). They are used on large work where neatness is not so important. Two uses for this type of nail are for making packing cases and wooden fencing.

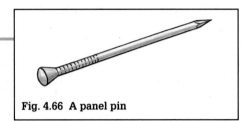

Fig. 4.66 A panel pin

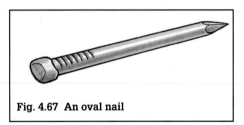

Fig. 4.67 An oval nail

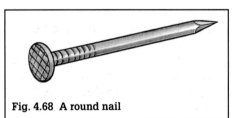

Fig. 4.68 A round nail

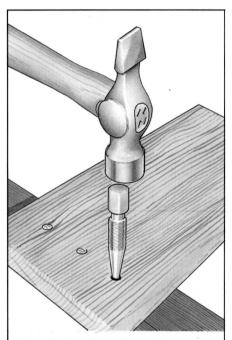

Fig. 4.69 A nail punch, punches nails below the surface

Nail pincers

Nail pincers are used to pull out nails. They can be used to pull out bent nails or nails that are in the wrong place. Place a piece of scrapwood under the tool to prevent it from marking the wood. Roll the pincers on the rounded jaws (see Fig. 4.70). The nail is then levered out. This action gives greater force than if you pull a nail out straight.

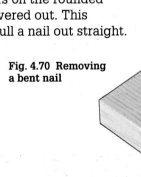

Fig. 4.70 Removing a bent nail

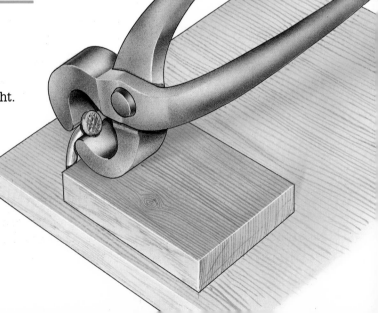

In D&T, you will learn to:
assemble a range of materials
use alternative means of joining materials
select and use appropriate methods of assembling a range of materials

Wood screws

Screwing is stronger than nailing, if it is done properly. In addition, the joined parts can be separated again if necessary by removing the screws. Screws can be used to fix wood, plastic or metal to wood. There are many small metal fastenings, such as hinges and locks which need to be attached to wood with screws.

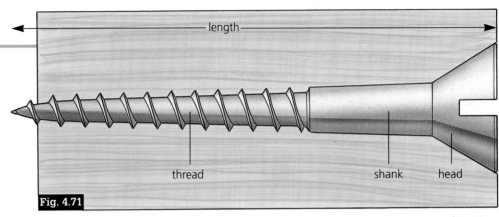

Fig. 4.71

length · thread · shank · head

Using a wood screw

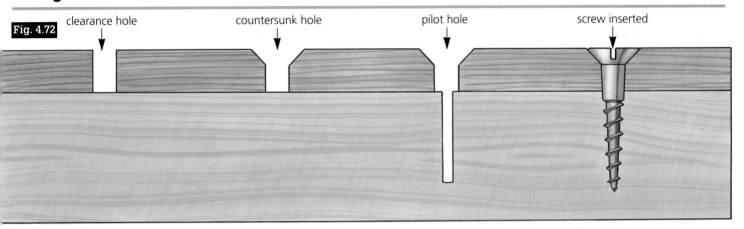

Fig. 4.72

clearance hole · countersunk hole · pilot hole · screw inserted

1. Drill a clearance hole through the top piece of wood or metal. It must allow the screw to pass through easily.

2. Drill a countersunk hole for the screw head so that it will finish flat (flush) with the surface and not stick out. If you are fastening a thin piece of metal to wood this cannot be done – a round-headed screw should be used instead (see Fig. 4.74).

3. Drill a pilot hole into the lower piece of wood. This hole should not go right through the wood. It is smaller than the width of the screw so that the threads will grip into the sides of the hole.

4. Put in the screw with the correct size of screwdriver.

If you are fastening two pieces of material together with more than one screw it will help you to drill all the holes in the top piece first. Then insert one screw before drilling the remaining pilot holes through the holes in the top piece. Using this method, you will always get the holes to line up exactly.

Types of screw

Countersunk-headed screws are the most common type of screw. They are used when the screw head must be flush with the surface. They are also used to fit hinges and brackets.

Round-headed screws are used when fitting thin metal to wood. The head sticks up from the metal, but it is rounded so it does not catch on clothing.

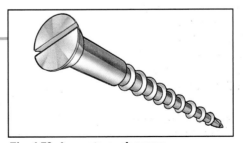

Fig. 4.73 A countersunk screw

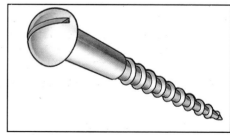

Fig. 4.74 A round head screw

EXTRAS

1. Make a list of all the things that you can find in the work area that are fastened with nails or screws.

Boxes and Frames

When you make objects using materials such as wood, metal and plastics you usually construct them from many different pieces. There are two main types of construction: one formed like a box, such as most containers, and the other formed like a frame, such as chairs and tables. For both these types of constructions there are special ways of joining the pieces together.

Box joints

Boxes are made from slabs of material joined together at the corners. Wood is usually glued and then pinned to make a strong, fixed corner (see Fig. 4.75a and b). Metal can be bent and folded like card and then joined together using pop rivets (see Fig. 4.76). Plastic containers can be made by using a line bender to fold thin sheets (see page 64) and, when cold, joining them together with a suitable glue (see Fig. 4.77).

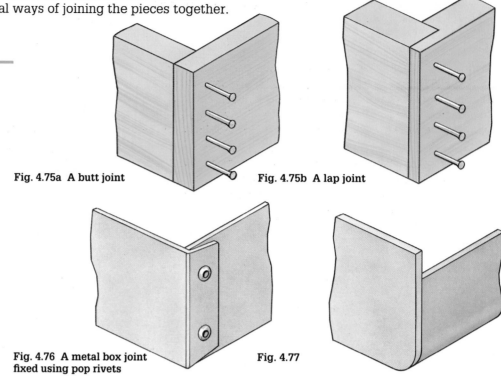

Fig. 4.75a A butt joint

Fig. 4.75b A lap joint

Fig. 4.76 A metal box joint fixed using pop rivets

Fig. 4.77

Frame joints

A large box made of solid wood could be used as a seat or a table but it would be very expensive to make, and very heavy. A frame box, however, is much lighter but still strong, and saves wood. There are many things made from frames, such as chairs, tables, climbing frames and ladders. Many different types of joints can be used to make frames, such as halving joints, bridle joints, mortice and tenon joints and dowel joints (see Fig. 4.78).

In D&T, you will learn to:

make judgements about products designed and made by others

use alternative means of joining materials

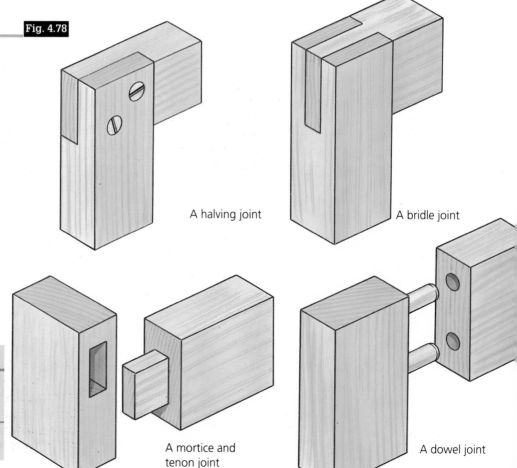

Fig. 4.78

A halving joint

A bridle joint

A mortice and tenon joint

A dowel joint

62

Moving joints

Fig. 4.79

You will often want to make objects with parts that move. There are different ways of joining these moving parts to the rest of the construction.

Hinges

Hinges are used to allow a lid or a door to open and close. Hinges have two parts joined by a pivot pin. One part is fixed (usually screwed) to the main part of the construction and the other to the door, lid, etc (see Fig.4.79). There are many types and sizes of hinge which your teacher will be able to show you. You must select the type that is most suitable for your needs. Look at the hinges on a room door and compare them with the hinges on a kitchen cabinet where they are often quite complex. Do all hinges work in the same way?

Fig. 4.80

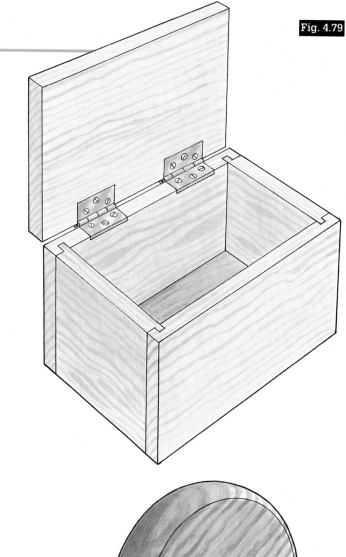

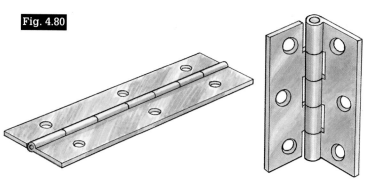

Rotating and sliding parts

Many of your projects will require you to make parts that will rotate, such as wheels. The wheel in Fig. 4.81 is held in place by two arms, one at each side, that are fixed. The axle is fastened to the wheel with glue and is free to turn in the holes in each of the arms. Alternatively, the axle could be fixed to the arms with glue, and the wheel left to turn freely on the axle.

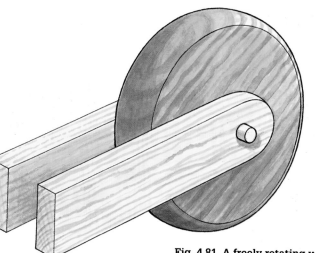

Fig. 4.81 A freely rotating wheel

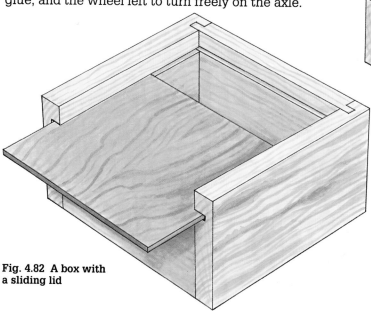

Fig. 4.82 A box with a sliding lid

Boxes can have sliding lids if grooves are cut in the sides, near the top (see Fig. 4.82). You must remember to cut the grooves before joining the box together. Plywood or acrylic are suitable materials to use as sliding box lids.

Shaping Plastics

Plastics are easy to shape and mould. When thermoplastics are softened by heating, they become very pliable. Strips of acrylic can even be tied in knots, like a ribbon, when they are hot. Remember that you must wear protective gloves when trying this.

Press forming

The temperature that is required to soften acrylic is around 160°C. This can be achieved by using an oven set at the correct temperature. (Remember to wear protective gloves.) Acrylic cools slowly, because it is a poor conductor of heat. It assumes the shape that it has been formed in when hot. Pressing the acrylic into a mould when soft can produce many different shapes – dishes and containers can be made very easily. A two-part former can be used to mould the acrylic (see Fig. 4.83). The mould must not be opened, however, until the acrylic is cool or it will not freeze into the new shape. The moulded acrylic can then be trimmed, if required.

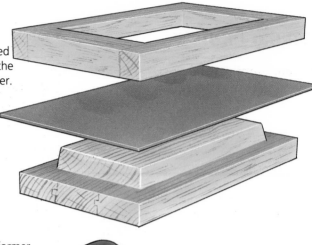

Fig. 4.83

1. The heated acrylic is placed between the mould and the frame of a two-part former.

2. The acrylic and two-part former are held in place using a vice, a press or cramps.

3. When cool, the moulded acrylic can be released from the two-part former and then trimmed.

Line bending

You may need to bend acrylic in straight lines, in the same way as you bend card. If you heat a whole sheet it is very difficult to bend the acrylic accurately. The easiest way is to use a line bender which only heats the area that needs bending (see Fig. 4.84). To do this, hold the acrylic over the strip heater and when the acrylic is soft, bend it gently. It is best if you can use a former to achieve the correct angle of bend (see Fig.4.85). This also allows you to hold the acrylic steady whilst it is cooling and stiffening.

Fig. 4.84

In D&T, you will learn to:
know the working properties of a range of materials
aim for a high quality of accuracy and presentation

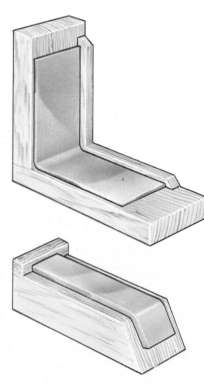

Fig. 4.85 Formers can help you bend acrylic accurately

Vacuum forming

Vacuum forming is another method of shaping plastics, using a special machine (see Fig. 4.86). The plastic sheet is heated evenly until soft, and then air pressure is used to shape it over a mould. The heating element is similar to the grill on a cooker and is usually movable to allow access to the machine. The sheet of plastic, acrylic or high-density polystyrene is fixed across the top of the machine by clamping. This must form an airtight seal. Below the plastic sheet in the air chamber is the mould. When the sheet is hot and soft, the heater is moved, the mould is raised and the air between the mould and the plastic sheet is evacuated by an air pump. The air pressure on the outside of the sheet then presses the plastic into close contact with the mould. The shape of the mould must be carefully designed to allow the plastic sheet to be easily removed, and the mould reused.

Fig. 4.86

Vacuum-formed components always have a shell of the same thickness throughout. This method of construction is extensively used in the packaging industry. Most food packaging and other small containers are formed by this method. Much larger machines are used to form acrylic baths, for use in houses.

Fig. 4.87 The hull of a Topper dinghy made by injection moulding

Injection moulding

Plastics can be shaped by forcing softened plastic into a specially shaped hole and allowing it to set. This process is called **injection moulding**. Many plastic items are produced by this method, including plastic kits for making model boats, cars, planes, etc. In these kits you can see the runners joining lots of small parts together. This is where the plastic has been forced into the mould. It is possible in a school workshop to produce small wheels and other items by injection moulding. It is not easy, however, to make the moulds for this process because they must be made from metal.

Injection-moulded components often have a complex shape and can range from being small to being very large. One of the largest injection mouldings is the hull of a Topper dinghy used in sailing schools (see Fig. 4.87).

Sticking Things Together

Glues are used to fasten materials together. When correctly applied and used, they can be permanent fastenings. Which glue you should use, and how you use it, depends on the materials being joined.

Tips for gluing

1 Clean the surfaces properly.

2 Use the correct glue.

3 Hold the surface firmly when applying the glue.

4 Firmly press together the surfaces and hold them in place while the glue sets.

5 Wait the correct length of time to allow the glue to dry before moving the object.

Fig. 4.88 A range of glues

Material	Glue	Process	Fig. 4.89
Wood	PVA	Apply to both surfaces (interior use) and cramp whilst setting	
Wood	Synthetic resin e.g. Cascamite	Apply to both surfaces (exterior use) and cramp whilst setting	
Paper	Glue stick e.g. Pritt Stick	Apply to one surface, press together	
Card	PVA	Apply to one surface, hold whilst setting	
Acrylic	*Acrylic cement e.g. Tensol No.6	Apply to both surfaces and press firmly together	
	*Tensol No.12	Apply liquid to joint line whilst pressed together	
Fabrics	Fabric glue e.g. Copydex	Apply to one surface, hold whilst setting	
Metal	Epoxy resin e.g. Araldite Rapid	Two-part mix, apply to both surfaces and hold together	

* Both these glues are highly flammable and must not be inhaled. They can also irritate the skin. You must ask your teacher for permission to use them. ⚠

Glue gun

A glue gun uses heated glue that will stick almost anything. You must be very careful when using this glue because it is very hot and will burn you if you touch it while it is still liquid.

In D&T, you will learn to:
use alternative means of joining materials
apply simple finishes appropriate to the materials used and to achieve a desired effect

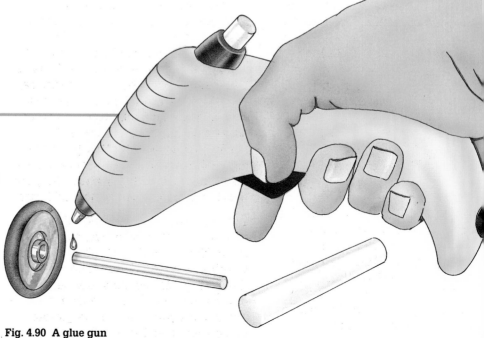

Fig. 4.90 A glue gun

Surface Finishes

The outer surface of any product must be pleasing to the eye, be able to resist wear and tear and, if necessary, withstand the ravages of the climate. The preparation and application of any protective layer is very important. If you are not careful, this last layer may spoil, rather than enhance the product you have been making.

The choice of finish depends on both the material being used and the use to which the product is to be put.

Wood

The surface must be smooth and dust-free. First, plane the surface until it is smooth, then rub along the grain with increasingly smoother grades of glass paper. Remove all marks and blemishes. Wood can then have a variety of preservative finishes:

- **Linseed oil** – rubbed into the surface. This is used on kitchen items and wooden bowls.

- **Varnish** – a clear or stained finish which allows the grain of the wood to be seen. This is used on hardwoods for both interior and exterior use.

- **Paint** – a coloured coating that is applied in layers. First a primer is applied, then an undercoat, and finally a gloss topcoat. This is resistant to the weather and so can be used outside as well as inside. Paint comes in a vast range of colours.

- **Polish** – beeswax is rubbed in with a soft cloth until a shiny finish is achieved. A polishing machine can also be used which has discs of fabric that polish the surface of the work and rub in the beeswax at the same time.

Fig. 4.91 Products used to finish and preserve materials

Acrylic

Acrylic is resistant to water and therefore does not need to be covered to preserve it. It must be polished, however, to show its colour and to make it look good. The aim of polishing acrylic is to smooth out all the scratches and imperfections until they are gone. First, a file or plane is used to remove all the saw marks. Then, using abrasive paper such as 'wet and dry' types, the acrylic is rubbed until all marks are removed. The acrylic can then be polished using a metal polish, such as Brasso or an acrylic polish. This is rubbed hard on the surface with a cloth, then polished off with a soft clean cloth. Acrylic can also be polished with a polishing machine.

Metal

Metals, such as steel, need to be protected to prevent them from rusting when exposed to the weather. The surface must be smooth, filed and rubbed with an emery cloth to remove all marks. The steel can then be painted in the same way as wood. It can be painted with a special quick-drying one-coat paint such as Hammerite, which is especially suitable for school use. Metals such as aluminium, brass, gold and silver do not rust, and are not often painted. They are polished to show their colour and lustre.

When polishing metal, first rub it with an emery cloth until all the marks are gone. Next, a buffing machine is used to rub a very fine abrasive polish over the surface. These machines can be dangerous if not used properly, so always ask your teacher first before using them (see Fig. 4.92).

Fig. 4.92 A buffing machine

5 FOOD

Fig 5.1

In this chapter you will find the answers to several questions about the food you eat, including:

1 What influences your choice of food?

2 How do social and religious customs affect the food you eat?

3 Does it matter what you eat?

4 What is the connection between food and good health?

5 Why do different members of the family need different food?

6 How do you prepare food so that it is appetising and safe to eat?

Choosing your food

If you were allowed to choose anything you like for your lunch today, what would you eat? Ask the person sitting next to you what their choice would be. Is it the same food or different?

Over the past 40 years the range and variety of food available in Britain have increased enormously. During the Second World War, and for several years after, many foods were not available or were **rationed** by the government. Today, Britain imports many different fruits and vegetables that grow in hot climates. For example yams, okra, root ginger, star fruit, lychees and lemon grass are now available in supermarkets. There is also a wide range of books and television programmes that show you how to cook recipes from different countries.

Fig 5.3 Shopping during the Second World War

In D&T, you will learn to:

recognise potential conflicts between the needs of individuals and of society

Fig 5.2

There are many factors relating to personal circumstances and changes in society that determine the food people eat today. Some of the reasons for the changes in people's eating habits since the 1940s are as follows:

● Many more people work outside the home, either full or part time, and want food that is quick to prepare and cook.

● There is more money to spend on ready-prepared or convenience food.

● Modern technology has increased the number of appliances in the home – food processors and microwave ovens, for example.

● Most people enjoy more leisure time, eat out in restaurants and buy take-away meals.

● Membership of the EC, improved transport and better refrigeration have all contributed to a wider selection of food in our shops.

● More people from ethnic groups live in Britain and have introduced a wide variety of foods.

Faith and Food

Customs, festivals and religious beliefs often determine the kind of food you eat. Christians celebrate the festivals of Christmas and Easter with special food such as turkey, Christmas pudding, mince pies, and chocolate eggs. Some Christians eat fish on Fridays instead of meat. During the season of Lent, Christians may give up a particular food.

Fig. 5.4 A Christmas dinner

During the eight days of the Passover, Jews celebrate the escape of the Israelites from their captivity in Egypt, as told in the Book of Exodus. Throughout this festival they eat unleavened bread, which is bread made without yeast or any ingredient that makes bread rise. Jews have strict laws which forbid them to eat certain foods such as pork, rabbit and shellfish. The meat they eat has to come from specially bred animals which are slaughtered in a particular way. This is called **kosher** food.

Fig. 5.5 The seder meal during the Passover recalls the exodus of the Israelites from captivity in Egypt.

Food offerings to gods and goddesses are an important part of religious practice for Hindus. During the Arti ceremony at the temple, after the food is offered to the gods and goddesses it is shared out to those present. This act reminds Hindus that God is in everyone. Hindus will not eat beef as they believe the cow is a sacred animal but will drink cow's milk and other dairy products. Some Hindus are vegetarians, believing it is wrong to kill animals.

Fig. 5.6 Offerings of food in the temple during Diwali

The Islamic festival Eid-ul-Adha recalls the willingness of Ibrahim to sacrifice his son, Ishmael, when Allah requested him to do so. Muslims eat lamb or goat at this festival as a reminder that Allah provided an animal sacrifice in the place of Ishmael. During the lunar month of Ramadan, Muslims fast and do not eat during daylight hours. Muslims do not eat pork or shellfish, and their meat is slaughtered in a particular way and is known as **halal** meat.

Fig. 5.7 Muslim teenagers celebrating Eid-ul-Fitr, the end of Ramadan. This food will be given to friends and family.

EXTRAS

1. Interview a grandparent, or someone of that generation, to find out what food they bought 40–50 years ago. Compare these foods with the food available today.

2. Choose a religion, and find out as much as you can about its main festivals and fast days. Make a list of the different foods associated with each of them.

Healthy Eating

What is meant by healthy eating? Are some foods actually unhealthy? Not really, but you could suffer from poor health if your diet does not include a variety of different food.

Write down everything you ate yesterday. Then, using coloured pens or pencils, place a tick next to each item of food using the following code:

Red – meat, fish, eggs, cheese and milk.
Yellow – fatty foods, such as fried food, crisps and biscuits.
Blue – potatoes, cereals, bread, rice and pasta.
Black – sweet food, such as chocolate bars, biscuits, cakes and sugary drinks.
Green – salad food, vegetables and fruit.

If you have plenty of ticks coloured red, blue and green, some yellow and not too many black the chances are that your diet is very healthy. However, if some colours are missing altogether you may need a more varied diet to enable you to grow and to give you all the energy you require.

Tuesday

Breakfast

cornflakes ✓
milk ✓
sugar ✓
orange juice ✓

Break

salt and vinegar crisps ✓
can of coke ✓

In D&T, you will learn to:

organise your working to complete the task on time

Fig. 5.8 The wheel of food and good health produced by the Dairy Produce Advisory Service

A balanced diet

The importance of eating a good variety of food has been recognised for a long time. Medical research has established beyond doubt the various links between health and diet. If a person suffers from toothache and has a lot of fillings they may be eating too much sugary food. Someone who is overweight may be eating too many sugary and fatty foods. A person suffering from constipation requires more fibre and fluids in their diet. Adults who suffer from high blood pressure or heart disease have to be careful about the type, and the quantity, of fat they eat. They should also eat less salt.

More fibre; less sugar, fat and salt

During the 1980s, experts on diet and health reported that the British diet contained too much sugar, fat and salt, and not enough fibre.

Fig. 5.9 a, b, c and d shows you foods that are low in sugar, fat and salt, and high in fibre. Choose a favourite recipe and see how healthy you can make it by cutting down the sugar, fat and salt content, and increasing the fibre. Using software or food tables, compare the traditional recipe with your improved recipe and see how the quantities of sugar, fat, salt and fibre have changed.

As well as altering recipes, you could improve your eating habits by:

1 Eating thicker slices of bread (preferably wholemeal) and less butter and sugary jams.
2 Eating more fruit and vegetables.
3 Choosing yoghurt instead of cream.
4 Eating less fried food.
5 Not adding extra salt to a meal when it's been served.

Fig. 5.9 (a) Low sugar, (b) Low fat, (c) Low salt, (d) High fibre

You should also look at how often you eat. There is a growing range of snack foods available and 'snacking' is becoming a popular part of people's diet. Snack foods such as crisps are very high in salt and fat, and chocolate bars are high in sugar and fat. If you must eat between meals, choose something healthy such as fruit. By eating a balanced diet and taking plenty of exercise (and not smoking) your body should be both healthy and fit.

EXTRAS

1. People with diabetes have a special diet. Find out as much as you can about diabetes. Then, make a list of the ingredients you would need to cook a meal for a friend who was diabetic.

Nutrients

You have learned that to remain healthy you should eat a wide selection of foods, but why does the body need such a variety? The study of food is called **nutrition**, and all food is made up of nutrients. They each have a name and a different job to do. The main nutrients are **proteins**, **fats** and **carbohydrates**.

Proteins

Fig. 5.10

Proteins are required for the growth and the repair of the body, and to fight infection. They form part of the blood and are found in every cell in the body. Proteins come from two sources:

1 Animal sources, such as meat, fish, eggs, cheese and milk.
2 Vegetable sources, such as peas, beans, lentils, nuts, soya, Quorn and tofu.

There are some types of proteins which it is essential to eat because they contain substances (amino acids) that the body cannot make for itself. Most foods contain small amounts of these proteins. The animal foods such as meat, fish, eggs, cheese and milk, and the vegetable food soya, are rich in these essential proteins in a form that the body can easily use. These proteins are said to have a **high biological value** (HBV). The proteins found in vegetable food such as peas, beans, lentils and nuts contain a smaller quantity of the essential proteins. These are said to have a **low biological value** (LBV). If two or more of these foods with LBV proteins are eaten together they may complement each other. That is, the proteins in the LBV foods, eaten together, becomes HBV proteins, for example lentil soup with bread, baked beans on wholemeal toast, tortilla and beans, rice and dahl.

Fats

Your body requires fats to keep it warm, to protect your vital organs such as your heart and kidneys, and to provide fuel which your body converts to energy.

Fats come from two sources:

1 Animal sources, such as butter, cheese, bacon, lard, suet, cream and some margarines.
2 Vegetable sources, such as corn oil, soya oil, rape-seed oil and poly-unsaturated margarines.

All fats are made up of smaller units called fatty acids. The various types of fatty acids determine how hard or soft the fat is at room temperature. Fats that are liquid at room temperature are called oils. There are many fatty acids, some of which are essential to the body, so fats should never be cut out of the diet completely (unless recommended by a doctor). However, too much fat in the diet can lead to heart disease and obesity.

For a product to be called a margarine it must contain 80 per cent fat. If it has less than 80 per cent fat, the product is called a 'low-fat spread'. Some of these are suitable for baking and spreading on bread, but others are not.

Fig. 5.11

Fig. 5.12

In a group, make some biscuits, cakes and scones using different types of fats, such as animal fat, margarine and low-fat spread. Label the food clearly so that you know which fat was used. When they are cooked, sample them! Draw a chart to show which food looked the best, which tasted the nicest, and which was the easiest to make. Do your friends agree? The high water content of the low-fat spread can affect the taste of the food. Can you suggest why?

EXTRAS

1. Protein deficiency is not found in Britain. Find out about the parts of the world where they do not have enough proteins. What are the protein deficiency diseases?

Carbohydrates

Your body requires carbohydrates to provide energy and dietary fibre to help digestion. Carbohydrates come from two sources:

1 Starches, such as bread, rice, pasta and cereals.
2 Sugars, such as honey, jam and syrup.

Carbohydrates consists of carbon, hydrogen and oxygen. They are made up of glucose blocks which provide your body with energy. It is important to ensure that most of your carbohydrate intake is from starchy foods and only a small amount from sugary foods. This is because starchy foods are a good source of dietary fibre, particularly when they are **unrefined** such as wholegrain cereals, wholemeal pasta, bread and rice. So as well as being a good energy source, starches keep your digestive systems healthy. Sugars are a good source of energy, but eating too much sugar can damage your teeth and make you overweight.

Fig. 5.13

Vitamins and minerals

Vitamins and minerals are not required in such large quantities as proteins, fats and carbohydrates, but they are nevertheless essential. Your body requires them to keep you healthy and to help you fight infections. A good mixed diet should ensure you are eating an adequate amount of vitamins and minerals. Different ones are contained in small amounts in most foods, and they all have a special function in keeping your body healthy.

Fig. 5.14

Vitamins

Vitamins can be divided into **fat-soluble** and **water-soluble** vitamins. The fat-soluble vitamins are vitamins A, D, E and K. They are found in all fatty foods such as meat, dairy foods and oily fish. Vitamin A is also found as carotene in 'red vegetables' such as carrots, tomatoes and red pepper. The water-soluble vitamins are the vitamin B complex and vitamin C. The B vitamins are found mainly in wholegrain cereals, yeast, meat and eggs. Vitamin C is found in fresh fruit, especially the citrus fruits, such as oranges, grapefruit and lemons. It is also found in vegetables such as green peppers, cabbages and potatoes.

Minerals

There are about 15 minerals that are essential for a person to remain healthy. The most important minerals are iron, calcium, fluoride and sodium. Iron is required to keep your blood healthy and transport oxygen around the body. It is found in liver, red meat, prunes, green vegetables, bread, eggs, baby cereals and chocolate. Calcium is important for the growth and strengthening of bones and teeth. It can be obtained from dairy foods, fish, and green vegetables. Fluoride is also required to maintain hard bones and teeth. It is found in water supplies in some parts of the country, and in seafood fish and tea. Sodium helps to keep the right balance of water in our body cells. It can be obtained from salt, bacon, fish, soya sauce and packet-mix soups and sauces.

Many other vitamins and minerals occur only in minute amounts but are still essential. These are called **trace elements**.

Fig. 5.15 Foods containing Iron, Calcium, Fluoride and Sodium

EXTRAS

1. Find out more about vitamins A, B, C, D and K. Draw and fill in a table showing which foods contain each of the vitamins and why the body needs them.

Food and Energy

Why is food so important? The simple answer is that without food your body would stop functioning, in the same way that a car without petrol cannot move.

Your body uses the food you eat to produce energy which in turn keeps your body fit and healthy. The substances in the food you eat are broken down during digestion and react with the oxygen we breathe to produce energy. This process is called oxidation and the rate at which oxidation occurs is called **metabolism**. The energy produced by oxidation is measured in kilojoules (1 kilojoule = 4.9 kilocalories):

1 gram protein = 17 kilojoules

1 gram fat = 38 kilojoules

1 gram carbohydrate = 16 kilojoules

Your body needs a certain amount of energy to carry out functions such as breathing, keeping a constant body temperature, pumping blood, digestion and growth (particularly in children). The rate at which energy is used for these basic activities is known as the **basal metabolic rate** (BMR). The BMR differs from person to person depending on, for example, body size, weight and shape. Males have a higher BMR than females, and children have a higher BMR than adults. For everyone the BMR accounts for more than half their energy needs.

A person's energy requirement is affected by age, sex, health and climate. It also depends on their work and leisure activities. Fig. 5.16 includes a list of the amount of kilojoules used per hour in various activities.

Activity	kJ used per hour
Sleeping	294
Office work	630
Housework	840
Tennis	1470
Cycling	1680
Road mending	1800
Football	2000
Swimming	2415

Fig. 5.16

In D&T, you will learn to:

devise an effective strategy for investigating a specific situation

use information sources in developing your proposals

evaluate the outcome of your activity against the original need, and propose modifications that would improve the overall quality of the outcome

The energy balance

The energy balance is the balance between the amount of energy a person takes into their body from the food they eat and the amount of energy they use. If a person eats too little food compared with the energy they use then they will lose weight. If they eat too much food compared with the energy they use, then the extra energy will be stored as fat, and they could become overweight.

You should try to keep an energy balance so that the food you eat is equal to the food your body requires to remain healthy and fit. In this way you maintain your normal body weight for your height. You can find out about average body weights by using the tables in Fig. 5.17 or a computer program such as *Energy, Food and Fitness.*

Males						
Age	Lower Height and Weight		Average Height and Weight		Upper Height and Weight	
11 years	134 cm	28 kg	142 cm	33 Kg	150 cm	41 Kg
12 years	139 cm	30 kg	147 cm	37 Kg	155 cm	46 Kg
13 years	144 cm	32 kg	152 cm	40 Kg	160 cm	51 Kg
14 years	152 cm	40 kg	161 cm	49 Kg	170 cm	60 Kg

Females						
Age	Lower Height and Weight		Average Height and Weight		Upper Height and Weight	
11 years	132 cm	28 kg	140 cm	33 Kg	148 cm	41 Kg
12 years	140 cm	31 kg	148 cm	38 Kg	156 cm	47 Kg
13 years	146 cm	34 kg	154 cm	42 Kg	162 cm	53 Kg
14 years	150 cm	40 kg	158 cm	49 Kg	167 cm	60 Kg

Fig. 5.17 Height and weight tables for 11 to 14 year olds

Recommended daily amounts

You have learned that you should have a variety of protein, fat and carbohydrate food in your diet, but how much of each one should you eat? It is possible to find out the amounts needed to keep the energy balance and to remain in good health. Recommended daily amounts (RDAs) are published in the UK by the Department of Health and Social Security and are updated frequently. They give a guide to the amount of energy required from the food you eat and the nutrients required to avoid deficiencies. The information is divided into specific groups according to sex, age, physical activity and health. RDAs are listed in food-table books and on computer programs.

Fig. 5.18

Obesity is a common complaint in all wealthy countries. Modern technology has improved transport systems and created many labour-saving devices. These have reduced the amount of energy used by most people in the past 60 years.

In a group, imagine that you were alive 60 years ago. Brainstorm a typical school day, from getting up to going to bed, and make a list of all the extra activities that you would do, compared with today.

Write down what you ate and drank during a 24-hour period. You will have to estimate what each portion of food weighed. Your teacher may be able to help by showing you how much some common foods weigh. Use food tables or a computer program to find out if your diet has a good balance of nutrients. Using the energy values stated in the tables it is possible to calculate your energy intake. The computer program will do the calculation for you. Compare your energy intake with the recommended daily amounts for your age, height, weight and sex. Do you need to alter the amount of certain nutrients you eat? Do you need to exercise more to burn up excess kilocalories?

Feeding Special Groups

Fig. 5.19

At certain times in their lives people will have special dietary needs. As people grow older their meal patterns and requirements change. The dietary needs of a baby, a toddler, a teenager and a pensioner are all different. There are other times, such as during pregnancy or illness, when people need a special diet for a short time. In addition, there are people who do not eat certain foods for religious, cultural or moral reasons.

Fig. 5.20

Babies

During the first three months of life, babies require only milk. This should be breast milk or formula (bottle) milk. After three or four months babies should begin to eat solid food. There are many commercially prepared baby foods (which are convenient when away from home) but many parents prefer to cook and purée (or sieve) suitable parts of the family meal, such as vegetables and fruits. It is important to remember that you should never add salt or sugar to baby food as it can be harmful to the baby. By nine months to a year babies can be eating similar food to the rest of the family.

In D & T, you will learn to:
know the importance of exploring needs and opportunities before proposing solutions
collate, sort, analyse, interpret and present information in a form appropriate to the purpose and the intended audience
organise your work, taking account of constraints
recognise that economic, moral, social and environmental factors can influence design and technological activities
recognise the relationship between price, cost, income and competition in the market for goods and services

Children

Young schoolchildren require plenty of protein foods as they are growing rapidly. They also need plenty of energy-rich foods to discourage them from eating between meals. A healthy and filling breakfast should be eaten and it may prevent snacking before lunch. As many children take a packed lunch to school, it is important to ensure it contains one third of the child's recommended daily amounts of nutrients.

Teenagers

Teenagers grow and develop rapidly and need a good supply of energy-giving foods, plenty of vitamins and minerals, especially vitamin C, calcium and iron. The teenage years are a time when too much junk food may be eaten at the expense of a good mixed diet, so it is important to take care what you eat.

Expectant and nursing mothers

A pregnant woman has to take care with her diet so that she eats enough to meet the requirements of her own body and that of a growing baby, but does not gain too much weight. To provide this nourishment she should eat a well-balanced diet, including foods high in fibre, rich in proteins and iron, and plenty of vitamins and minerals.

During pregnancy a woman should not drink alcohol (or smoke) as this can damage the baby.

When breast-feeding, a woman should consume extra water, proteins, vitamins and minerals – especially calcium and iron. Slimming diets should be avoided as they can cause tiredness and reduce the milk supply.

Elderly people

Most elderly people continue to eat normal, balanced diets. They tend to be less active than in their younger years and therefore require less food. They still need, however, the same amounts of minerals and vitamins. Some elderly people experience difficulties in health or personal circumstances which make preparing meals a chore. Social problems include a lowering of income and eating alone (which can lead to a lack of interest in preparing or cooking food). Practical problems may include less mobility (making it difficult to go shopping), finding food products in sizes suitable for one person, difficulty in preparing and cooking food due to arthritis or shakiness, and digestive problems. Many elderly people rely on 'meals on wheels' to provide them with a hot meal during the day.

Fig. 5.21

Vegetarians

Vegetarians are people who will not eat meat, poultry or fish. **Vegans** will not eat any animal products, even milk, cream and cheese. All their food must come directly from plants. Vegetarianism is becoming more common as increasing numbers of people are questioning the economic use of land and the treatment of animals, and believe that a vegetarian diet is healthier than a non-vegetarian diet. A well-balanced vegetarian diet of cereals, pulses, nuts, fruits and leafy vegetables contains less fat and more fibre than most diets containing meat. However, vegans may have to take Vitamin B12 supplement as this vitamin is not usually found in vegetable foods.

Fig. 5.22

EXTRAS

1. Make a survey of food advertising on television and in magazines. Does it encourage children and teenagers to eat a healthy diet?

2. Make a survey of the prices of special 'vegetarian' products (vegetarian burgers, for example). If they are more expensive than their meat equivalents, can you explain why?

Preparing Food

In your Food Technology area there will be a store of equipment to help you to carry out certain tasks when preparing food. There are some tasks you will carry out regularly, such as measuring, stirring, chopping, grating and slicing. It is important to know which equipment is the most efficient or suitable for your task.

Choosing equipment

In a small group make a list of a range of equipment you would use when preparing food. Record on a chart the equipment suitable for measuring, stirring, chopping, grating, slicing, peeling and whisking. Your chart should include a large variety of small equipment. Fig 5.24 gives you an example of how to start.

Fig. 5.23

EQUIPMENT	measuring	stirring	chopping	grating	slicing	peeling	whisking
Food Processor		 ●	 ●	 ●	 ●		 ●
Spoon	 ●	 ●					
Fork							 ●

Fig. 5.24

When preparing food, some equipment is chosen for safety reasons. For example, when stirring hot food you should use a wooden spoon and not a metal spoon. This is because wood is a bad conductor of heat, so the handle of the wooden spoon will not get hot. Metal is a good conductor of heat so the handle of the metal spoon will soon become too hot and burn your fingers.

The recipe instructions will affect your choice of equipment. You may have to measure the ingredients with spoons or cups instead of scales, or you may be asked to grate your ingredients coarsely or finely.

Fig. 5.25 A demonstration of kitchen equipment at the Ideal Home Exhibition

In D&T, you will learn to:
use information and experience gained from appraising products
produce a documented plan for their work, including an analysis of the resources required and a time schedule
recognise the purpose of equipment, to understand their handling characteristics, and the basic principles upon which they work
test simple objects to determine performance

Technology has contributed enormously to food preparation, and it is now possible to purchase all kinds of gadgets to save energy and time in the kitchen. If the opportunity arises, visit your local hardware store, the Ideal Home Exhibition or a similar trade fair to see kitchen equipment being demonstrated. The Consumers Association produce a magazine called *Which* and it reports on the performance of a wide range of equipment and services. It is a helpful source of information if you wish to buy a costly item for the home.

Kitchen gadgets

Kitchen gadgets include food processors, blenders, mixers, liquidisers, scales and potato peelers. The manufacturers of all these gadgets claim that they are quick and efficient. Only the user however, can decide if the total time, (including washing up and care of the appliance) and the purchase and running costs make them worthwhile.

Fig. 5.26 A bean slicer

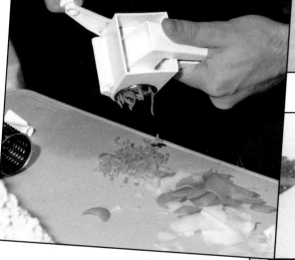

Fig. 5.27 A grater

In a group, devise a test to compare two pieces of kitchen equipment doing the same task. For example, (a) a potato peeler and a knife, for peeling a potato, (b) a food processor and a hand cheese grater, for grating cheese, or (c) a food processor and a hand whisk, for whisking egg-white. Record your findings in a table. Decide in the group the headings you wish to use, for example Time to prepare, Carry out task and wash up, Safety, and The quality of the result. Find out the cost of the items of equipment and make an evaluation based on your findings.

Fig. 5.28 Pupils testing and comparing equipment

EXTRAS

1. Imagine you have £200 to spend on kitchen equipment for preparing food. What would you buy, and why?

Mixing Foods

Fig. 5.29

Mixing is an enjoyable and interesting part of food preparation. Depending on the ingredients used (whether they are solid or liquid) and how they react with one another, mixing changes their appearance and properties. Usually it is impossible to reverse the mixing process. It is important to understand the changes that take place so that you can produce good results every time you cook.

There are different changes which take place when you cook food. These are explained on pages 84 and 85. Here we are concerned only with mixing.

Emulsions

Here are some experiments for you to try.

In a food processor bowl, place –
3 tablespoons olive oil
1 tablespoon vinegar
1 teaspoon sugar
1 teaspoon mustard
1 teaspoon lemon juice
a pinch of salt

Process together for 30 seconds. Then transfer the ingredients to a screw-top jar. Stand the jar on a surface and observe what happens.

You have made a french dressing. You will see that the vinegar and the oil have separated out. Which is on the top and which is on the bottom? As you can see, the two liquids do not mix well and need to be shaken immediately before serving to mix them together.

	In D&T, you will learn to:
	combine materials to create others with enhanced properties
	work together to establish criteria for appraisal of design and technological activity
	know that objects are changed by the forces applied to them

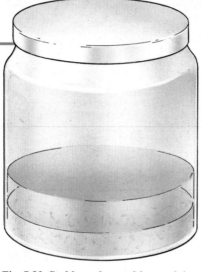

Fig. 5.30 Stable and unstable emulsions

We call this kind of mixture an **emulsion**. This is an **unstable emulsion** because the drops of oil do not stay evenly distributed throughout the vinegar.

To stop the mixture separating out you need to add an emulsifier. This makes the mixture a **stable emulsion**. For example, you add egg yolk when making mayonnaise because egg yolk contains lecithin – the most common emulsifier. Lecithin has been given the E number E 322. (An E number refers to specific food additives that are recognised by the European Community.)

Now experiment with the following ingredients and notice the difference.
2 size-3 egg yolks
1 teaspoon dry mustard
salt and pepper
250 mls olive oil
1 tablespoon vinegar

Using a food processor, place the eggs, egg yolk, mustard and seasoning into the processor bowl. Process together for 5 seconds. With the machine running, add the oil (drop by drop, to prevent the mixture curdling). As it begins to thicken, the oil can be added more quickly. When the mixture is thick and creamy you can add the vinegar. Transfer your ingredients to a screw-top jar. You have made a mayonnaise, a stable emulsion that does not separate when left to stand.

Solutions and suspensions

Other liquid mixtures are called **solutions** and **suspensions**. The following experiment shows you the difference between these mixtures.

Make a cup of instant coffee and a cup of coffee made with ground coffee beans (using a cafetiere, a percolator or a filter coffee maker). Some people call this 'real coffee' and it can have a variety of flavours depending upon the country of origin, and the type of coffee beans used. When the coffees have cooled down pour them into glasses. What difference can you see between the two glasses? The instant coffee will have dissolved completely in the hot water, and is a solution. The grounds in the 'real' coffee remain as very small particles which will settle on the bottom of the glass. As the grounds are suspended in the liquid we call it a suspension.

Fig. 5.31

Sauces and gravies

Another important process you need to understand when cooking is how to thicken liquids. When making a sauce, gravy or custard you want it to have the correct consistency (that is, smooth and not lumpy, and not too thick or too thin). The thickening agent in these mixtures is starch, and it is found in flour (wheat or corn flour) in the form of granules. When these granules are mixed with water or milk and heated, they burst, absorb the liquid and thicken the mixture. This is called **gelatinisation**. To avoid a lumpy mixture it is important to blend the flour with a little cold liquid first, and to stir continuously whilst heating to make sure the granules are separate and moving in the liquid.

Mix a teaspoon of flour with 2 teaspoons of water in a basin. Place a drop of this mixture on to a microscope slide. Cover with a cover slip and place under the microscope. Can you see the granules of starch? Make a drawing of them. Heat the mixture until it has thickened and leave it to cool. Then have a look at a drop of this mixture under the microscope. Have the granules swollen and burst?

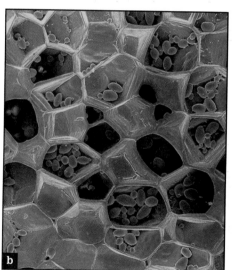

Fig. 5.32 **Potato starch grains seen under a microscope (a) before cooking and (b) after cooking**

Other mixtures you may need to be familiar with involve the mixing of flour with fat and possibly sugar, eggs and milk to make a variety of pastries, cakes, scones and biscuits. The basic ingredients to make these foods are similar, and the method of mixing may also be the same (especially if an all-in-one method is chosen using a processor). The results, however, are quite different because the basic ingredients are used in different quantities.

Working in groups, look at recipes for scones, biscuits and cakes. Compare the mixtures. Make a note of the various types of fat and flour, the proportions of fat to flour and other ingredients used. In your group, make a variety of these mixtures using different fats and flours. Evaluate your results. Why are some fats and flours more suitable for certain mixtures than others?

EXTRAS

1. Research and experiment with a yeast mixture. Explain the reaction that takes place during bread making. Why is it important to use 'strong' plain flour?

Cooking Food

Think about the meals you ate yesterday. Was the food contained in them raw or cooked? In some parts of the world, it is usual to eat more raw food than we do in Britain. For example, the Eskimos and the Japanese enjoy raw fish, and many Africans chew raw vegetables and shoots. This chewing action on raw foods strengthens and develops the jaw, and prevents many of the dental problems that Western people experience.

Why, then, do we cook some food? The main reasons include:

- To make food tender and easier to digest
- To make food taste better
- To destroy bacteria
- To add variety to meals

Transferring heat

Heat is generated by gas, electricity or solid fuel. It is transferred into the food by **radiation**, **conduction** and **convection**.

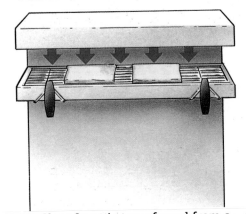

Radiant heat is transferred from a grill or an element, as in a toaster, which cooks the outside of the food quickly. Care has to be taken when grilling foods not to overcook them, as this makes them dry.

Convection currents occur when the air inside an oven is heated by either the gas burner or electric elements.

The hot air rises and is replaced by cooler air which in turn heats up and rises. This circular motion of hot, moving air creates zones in the oven. The hottest zone is at the top of the oven and the coolest zone is at the bottom. Convection currents in liquids boil or poach food.

Conduction takes place when heat is transferred through a solid object. An example of this is a frying pan on the hob. Pans are made from different materials, such as stainless steel, aluminium, copper and cast iron, and some are better conductors of heat than others. Which pan is best?

Choose pans made from different materials that are in your food technology room. Boil 1 litre of water in each one. Time how long it takes for the water to boil in each pan and draw a graph to show the results. Place the pans in rank order, according to how well they conduct heat.

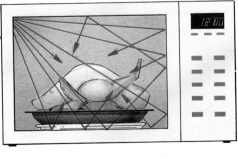

Microwaves

Microwave ovens cook by means of electromagnetic waves which penetrate the food, causing the molecules to vibrate and heat up. Microwave cooking is very fast compared to conventional cooking and uses much less energy.

Energy-saving appliances

Energy-saving cooking appliances include **pressure cookers**, microwave ovens and combination microwave ovens. A pressure cooker is a large sealed pan in which food is cooked by a combination of boiling and steaming. Steam is forced into the food at high pressure. As the pressure increases so does the temperature at which the water will boil. At this higher temperature the food cooks more quickly. This method of cooking also helps prevent the loss of nutrients from the food. The pressure is controlled by a system of weights.

The most advanced microwave oven is called a **combination microwave**. This is because it can be programmed to cook by microwave only, by convection only as in a conventional oven, or by a combination of the two. The advantages include energy and cost saving, and the ability to brown food.

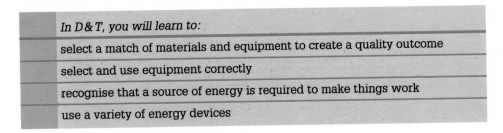

In D&T, you will learn to:

select a match of materials and equipment to create a quality outcome

select and use equipment correctly

recognise that a source of energy is required to make things work

use a variety of energy devices

Choosing a cooker

A cooker is one of the most expensive items in the home. There are very many types to choose from so how does a person decide which one to buy? First, they have to consider how much they have to spend. Second, which fuel is available to them. Gas cookers are often more expensive to buy than electric cookers, but gas cookers can be up to three times cheaper to run. Find out the cost of a unit of gas and a unit of electricity.

Ask if your technology department has a Telectric Monitor. It can be plugged into any electrical appliance to measure the energy cost of running it. Try the following experiment. Compare the cost of heating 1 litre of water to boiling point in a traditional kettle and in a jug kettle. What is the cost and which is the more energy-saving device? Your department may also have a Labgas Meter. Ask your teacher to show you an experiment to measure the cost of cooking by gas.

The third consideration when choosing a cooker would be the number of people in the family, and their particular preferences for the different features. Many features on a

Fig. 5.34 Pupils using a Labgas meter

modern cooker are concerned with saving energy. Others are linked with personal preferences – for a high-level rather than a low-level grill, for example, or a rotisserie for kebabs and spit-roasted chicken.

Energy-saving features

A **halogen hob** cooks by light. The halogen lamp is situated under a ceramic hob. When it is switched on, it heats up rapidly and therefore saves energy. It does, however, rely on pans with a perfectly flat base to ensure maximum efficiency.

Induction hobs involve cooking by magnetism. They are very expensive, but they do have many advantages over conventional cookers. Energy is transferred magnetically from an induction coil underneath the ceramic surface into the saucepan itself, leaving the hob cool. They are safer, quicker, easier to clean and almost twice as efficient as conventional hobs. Only pans made of cast iron, steel and some stainless steel should be used.

Fig 5.35 shows some pictures of gas and electric cookers and a list of popular features. Copy the pictures and label the features using the list below.

Fig. 5.35

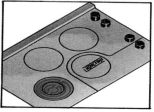 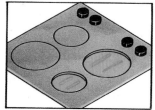 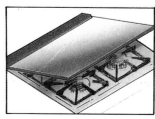

High-level grill	Automatic ignition
Autotimer	Fan-assisted oven
Minute minder	Plate-warming rack
Dual rings	Warming drawer
Ceramic hob	Glass lid/cover
Halogen hob	Oven/panel lights
Induction hob	Stay-clean lining

Cooking Around the World

In recent years developed countries have adopted a whole range of cooking methods from other countries. For example, in Britain ordinary pubs and cafés now offer pizza, lasagne, kebabs, Spanish omelette, curry, hamburgers, spare ribs, stir-fry vegetables and samosas. All over the world an interesting variety of food is prepared and cooked in many different ways.

Many people in Thailand, India, and China still use a small oven heated by charcoal or other solid fuel. Meat and vegetables are chopped finely and cooked together for a short time. The Chinese call their cooking pot a **wok**. It is large, and rounded at the bottom and sides and fits on a stand over the hot-plate. Oil can be heated in the bottom to stir-fry vegetables, or water can be put in with a rack on top to steam food using a lid to hold in the steam. This method of cooking has now become popular in this country.

Fig. 5.36 Cooking with a wok in China

In Australia, people enjoy grilled beef steaks, and because of the hot climate, cooking out of doors on a **barbecue** is very popular. Cooking and eating outside in this way is also enjoyed by many Americans and Europeans during the summer. In Canada you can pull off the highway into a picnic area which has built-in barbecues. All you need to do is to collect some wood for fuel and you can grill your sausages.

Fig. 5.37 A barbecue in Australia

Greece also has a hot climate and many meals are eaten out of doors at cafes called **tavernas**. Seafood such as octopus is very popular and it can be seen drying in the sun. The seafood is usually eaten with salad containing peppers, olives and fetta (goat's milk) cheese. It is often followed by fruit, such as figs, peaches and watermelons.

The strangely named **Bombay duck** is a fish that is caught in the Indian Ocean and hung on bamboo canes to be dried by the sun. It can be fried or eaten as part of a curry meal.

In D&T, you will learn to:

recognise the historical and cultural background to design and technological developments

Fig. 5.38 Eating outdoors in Greece

Fig. 5.39 Tortillas

In Mexico, the staple food is a **tortilla**. It is a type of bread made from maize which has a round and flat shape. It is eaten with most meals, and sometimes spread with other food and rolled up like a pancake. You can see it being cooked in street markets.

Fig. 5.40 Kebabs being cooked in Iran

Iranians like to eat **kebabs**, which are cubes of meat and vegetables placed on a skewer and grilled. The food is often marinated in a spicy sauce before being cooked over an open air fire.

Fig. 5.41 A child eating matoke

In poorer parts of the world such as Uganda, the staple food is a porridge made from plantains. It is called **matoke** and is cooked in the open air in large metal containers which stand on stones over a fire.

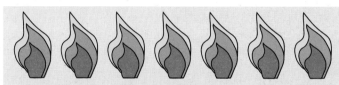

From fire to microwaves

No one really knows when food was first cooked. It must have been thousands of years ago, perhaps not long after fire was discovered. Later, the invention of clay pots made more cooking methods possible. This was just the first of a whole series of technological developments such as ovens, gas, electricity and pressure cookers. Each new invention made cooking easier, quicker, more hygienic, cheaper or more varied. The newest development, microwave ovens (invented in the 1950s), has revolutionized cooking methods all around the world.

EXTRAS

1. Choose a country and find out which are its staple food and how they are prepared, cooked and served.

Presentation of Food

In this chapter you have learnt about choosing food to ensure good health, and about preparing, mixing and cooking food. It is just as important to make sharing a meal an enjoyable experience. The way the food is presented can make all the difference. Throughout the year special meals are carefully planned and prepared to celebrate various family occasions and festivals. However, the presentation of food is also important in everyday meals.

Fig. 5.42

People have expectations about the colour, flavour, aroma and texture of foods. Imagine being presented with new potatoes that were green in colour and strawberry flavoured. Could you eat them?

Conduct a little experiment with some mashed potato, boiled rice and stewed apple. Colour and flavour them to make them unusual. Ask three of your friends to taste them. Can they bear to eat them? What are their favourite foods. Do they like them because of their colour, flavour, texture or for any other reason?

Having considered (or imagined) the results of the experiment, you will be aware of the importance of how food looks when it is served. It should look attractive and conform to your expectations regarding colour, flavour, aroma and texture.

Fig. 5.43

Decorating food

The art of decorating food is called **garnishing** for savoury dishes, and **decorating** for sweet dishes. Here are some examples of garnishes: chopped parsley or chives, lemon twists or wedges, cucumber twists, tomato water lilies, celery curls, gherkin fans, fringed spring onions and flower-shaped radishes. Ingredients used for decoration include: glacé cherries, angelica, chopped nuts, crystalised fruits, flaked or moulded chocolate, fruit, vermicelli and various sugared decorations. Make a list of dishes that could be garnished or decorated using the above examples.

In D & T, you will learn to:
consider, when selecting and using materials, their physical and aesthetic properties, availability and cost, and the product being made
apply simple finishes appropriate to the materials used and to achieve a desired effect

Fig. 5.44

Special meals

When you wish to make a special meal to entertain your friends, you will choose dishes to accommodate their likes, the money you have to spend, the time of year, and how formal it should be, for example a summer barbecue or a dinner party. You should cook dishes within your capability, and remember to try out a new recipe before you make it for a special occasion. A simple dish attractively served and decorated is better than an advanced technique that hasn't worked, such as a sunken soufflé.

When you are preparing a special meal, it is very important to be organised. Make a list of ingredients that can be purchased in advance, and those which have to be bought on the day such as salad, bread or cream. Then, make a time plan for both the day before, and for the day you are serving the meal. Remember to allow time for foods to set and defrost, and to do as much as you can earlier in the day, including laying the table.

Menu: chicken escalopes, Brussels sprouts, new potatoes; raspberry trifle.

Preparation the day before:
- Flatten the escalopes and coat in breadcrumbs.
- Prepare the potatoes and Brussels sprouts.
- Make some garlic butter to serve with the escalopes.
- Make the trifle.

Preparation one hour before:
- Decorate the trifle with whipped cream and raspberries.
- Fry the chicken escalopes.
- Put the potatoes and Brussels sprouts on to boil for 10-15 minutes
- Put the cooked escalopes in a serving dish and keep warm.

Fig. 5.45 A time plan

How the food is served will also add to the success of your entertaining. If you are having a buffet, it is important to make sure the food is in bite-sized pieces. When you lay the table try to have a clean and ironed table-cloth. Think about the dishes in which you will serve the food. Try to arrange a colour scheme with complementary serviettes and a small flower arrangement for the table centre. If you are hosting a children's party you may have a particular theme for the food and decorations. Allow time for your own personal preparation so you can be a calm and unruffled host or hostess to your guests.

Imagine you are responsible for planning aircraft meals. Plan a hot meal with a main course and pudding. What are your restrictions? How have technological developments helped your job? How will your meal be packed and presented?

Fast-food restaurants

Eating habits have changed with changing lifestyles, advances in food technology, transport, food hygiene and influences from other countries. Fast-food restaurants are growing in popularity in Britain following their success in the USA. Each fast-food chain presents its food in distinctive disposable packaging. The food is strictly standardised by the chain so that at all its branches each product will always have the same appearance and flavour. List the types of fast-food restaurants that are available in your area and discuss the quality of the food, its presentation and packaging, and whether you feel the restaurants are a vital part of the community. Would you make any changes? Could the packaging be improved? Can you say what food trends will develop as you grow older?

Fig. 5.46

EXTRAS

1. Herbs and spices are used to improve the flavour and presentation of food. Find out about the different varieties and their uses in cooking.

Food Safety

Your health depends largely on the food you eat. But what if the food you eat makes you ill and gives you food poisoning? What has gone wrong, and how can you try to make sure it doesn't happen again? Let's follow your food from production to eating and see what steps can be taken at each stage to prevent food poisoning.

As soon as food has been harvested or slaughtered it will start to decay or spoil. The action of enzymes inside the food continues to break down the cells and ripen foods until they rot. At the same time, the outside of food is attacked by moulds, yeasts and bacteria. If the food is not processed and stored in the right way it can cause food

poisoning. The amount of harm that can be caused depends on the type of bacteria present, and the age and health of the person eating the food. Two kinds of bacteria you may have heard of are salmonella and listeria. Salmonella is found in poultry, cooked meat and meat pies, and listeria is found in soft cheeses, ice-cream, and cook-chill meals.

There are strict hygiene rules and quality-control regulations for the packaging, transportation and sale of food. At the point of sale you become responsible for food safety until the food is eaten. To prevent poisoning you must take particular care of food storage, personal hygiene and general cleanliness.

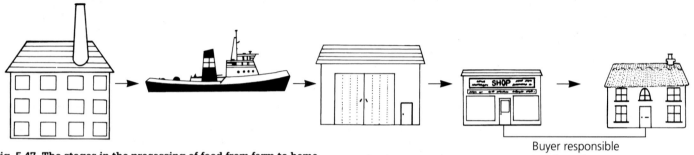

Buyer responsible
for safety

Fig. 5.47 The stages in the processing of food from farm to home

Food storage

If bacteria are to grow and multiply they need warmth, food, moisture and time to develop. If one or more of these factors is absent then the risk of food poisoning is lessened. Chilled foods should be placed in a refrigerator and stored at below 5°C. Frozen foods need to be stored in a freezer at −18°C. Dry foods should be stored in cupboards and eaten by the recommended dates on the packaging. Foods that are waiting to be eaten hot should be kept at a temperature of at least 63°C.

Personal and general cleanliness

Always wash your hands with hot, soapy water before preparing food, after using the lavatory or blowing your nose. Cover any cuts you have with a plaster. Do not stroke pets or smoke in the kitchen. Boil dishcloths and change tea towels regularly.

In pairs, look at the kitchen in Fig. 5.48. Make a list of the things that you think are unhygienic. Design a poster or leaflet to promote hygiene in the kitchen.

Fig. 5.48

	In D & T, you will learn to:
	ensure that the working area is well ordered and safe, and that equipment is well maintained
	recognise that materials and equipment need to be safely stored and maintained
	identify hazards in the working environment and to take appropriate action if dangerous situations occur

Good bacteria?

Not all bacteria are bad, and we rely on some to give us some of the food we enjoy. Two examples are yoghurt and cheese. Find a recipe for making yoghurt and draw a flow chart to show the stages in its production. Using the recipe, make your own yoghurt. The bacteria responsible for its success are called **lactobacillus bulgaricus** and **streptococcus themophillus**. Do you prefer your home-made yoghurt to a bought variety? Compare both products' cost, texture and flavour.

Preserving food safely

Fig. 5.49

For centuries it was necessary to preserve food in various ways so that people could survive during the winter when there was a limited supply of fresh food. Today, food can be imported from all over the world allowing many fruit and vegetables to be bought throughout the year. However, food is still preserved to keep it safely for long periods of time, to make seasonal food available all year round, to add variety to your diet and simply because some people like the taste. The box below contains the most common methods of preserving food safely.

Drying by removing moisture. Examples: dried apricots, dried tomatoes and prunes.	**Freezing** which inhibits bacterial growth and keeps food for a long time. Examples: fish, meat and oven-ready foods.	**Using chemicals** such as salt, vinegar and sugar. Examples: salted beef, pickled onions and marmalade.
Heating such as pasteurization and canning. Examples: UHT milk, canned fruit and vegetables.	**Irradiating** by treating foods with gamma rays to kill bacteria. Examples: strawberries and shellfish.	**Smoking** by drying foods in smouldering smoke. Examples: poultry, salmon, kippers, ham, bacon, nuts and cheese.

Additives

Food technology is all about changing foods to suit people's needs and demands. You would probably not like to eat white custard, separated mayonnaise or bland-flavoured strawberry sauce. You would also expect many foods to keep for several days. It is because of these needs that additives are added to food. There are different kinds of additives for different purposes. There are colourings, flavourings, emulsifiers, preservatives and nutritional additives, such as vitamins and minerals.

Fig. 5.50

In a group, collect some labels from different foods and look up the names or numbers of the additives in leaflets, or the book called *E for Additives*. Find out what their chief purpose is, for example, colouring, flavouring or emulsifying. Which additives do you think are the most important. Are they all necessary?

EXTRAS

1. There has been an increase in the number of people getting food poisoning in the last 10 years. How do you think the following factors have contributed to this increase?
a) lifestyle
b) bulk shopping
c) the increased use of convenience foods
d) the trend to remove additives, especially preservatives, from food.

2. Research and identify recent changes in food laws under the 1990 Food Safety Act. You can get a copy from the Environmental Health Department.

Consumer Needs

What is a consumer? Have you recently had your hair cut or been out for a meal? Perhaps you have bought some new shoes or a loaf of bread. In all of these instances you have been a consumer. In the first two examples you were buying a service and in the second two examples you were buying goods.

The main factors that determine what food you would buy as a consumer are:

● How much money you have to spend.
● What cooking facilities you have available.
● How much storage and freezer space you have in your home.

Fig. 5.51 A pick-your-own fruit and vegetable farm

Budgeting

Managing your money is called **budgeting**. You have to balance your income with your expenditure. It is also wise, if possible, to save some of your income for emergencies.

If you have a limited income, the following guidelines will help you budget:

1 Plan your meals ahead and make a shopping list.
2 Look for competitive prices and 'own brands' of particular products.
3 Use foods in season.
4 You can save money (if you have enough storage space) by buying pick-your-own fruit and vegetables, freezer packs and bulk-buy goods.

Investigate some bulk-buy foods and calculate the savings. What is the saving, if any, on buying an E10 box of soap powder rather than the equivalent E3 sizes? Find out when various foods are in season.

Cooking facilities

Cooking facilities vary considerably according to your circumstances. At home you may have a gas, electric or solid fuel cooker (see Fig. 5.52a), and a microwave oven. You may also have several smaller items of equipment such as a deep-fat fryer, a sandwich toaster or a slow cooker. As a student or a single person living alone in a bed-sit or flat, you may only have the use of a hot-plate (see Fig. 5.52b). Your choice of food will be determined by your facilities.

Fig.5.52a

Fig.5.52b

In D&T, you will learn to:
set objectives and identify resources and constraints
work with a variety of media to produce graphic outcomes
recognise that the preferences of consumers can change
plan a simple budget

Meal patterns

Another major consideration, when thinking of consumer needs, is the amount of time you are able to spend preparing and cooking food. This is linked with your own particular lifestyle. How have people's lifestyles changed over the past 50 years? Do a survey in your class to find out how many members of each family are out of the house at different times of the day. Do some people work shifts? What effect does this have on meal patterns? Most families would agree that mealtimes are less formal and strict than they used to be. Others regret the lack of time to discuss the events of the day with each other and share in any problem solving. In some cases, each member of the family eats on their own in front of the television and a family meal around the dining table is seldom possible.

Fig. 5.53

Labelling

Pressure groups are constantly asking for more information to be available on food labels. The 1984 Food Labelling Act requires pre-packed food to inform the buyer of:

1 The name and type of the product.
2 The ingredients in descending order of weight, that is largest first.
3 The name of additives or their E numbers.
4 The sell-by, or best-before date.
5 The name and address of the manufacturer.
6 The weight or volume of the food.
7 Storage instructions.
8 Place of origin.
9 Any preparation instructions if required.

Some products also include information about the suitability of the food for slimmers, vegetarians, or diabetics.

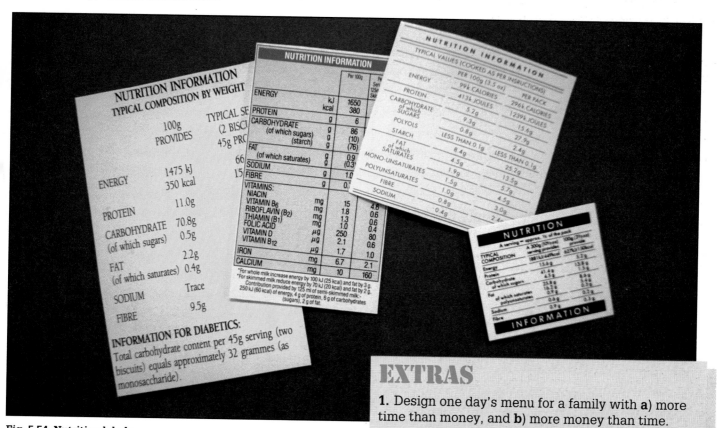

Fig. 5.54 Nutrition labels

EXTRAS

1. Design one day's menu for a family with a) more time than money, and b) more money than time.

How Food is Sold

In many ways, food and food products are just like any other product. Selling food can involve market research, promoting an image, advertising, and creating tempting displays (see pages 100–107). Food is also covered by consumer protection laws.

Consumer protection

In this country there are several laws controlling the sale of food. These concern labelling (see page 93), weights and measures, and hygiene and storage (see page 90). If customers have any complaints, there are various organisations to turn to, ranging from the local Citizen's Advice Bureau in the high street, to the Trading Standards or Environmental Health departments of the council, or the Office of Fair Trading.

Fig.5.55 Advertising milk on television

Butchers, bakers and supermarkets

Food shopping takes up a considerable amount of the family budget and time. Most families go to their local supermarket to buy the bulk of their weekly shopping.

	In D&T, you will learn to:
	gather, select and organise information for use in designing
	explore a range of potential solutions before selecting one
	know how designers and technologists have produced ideas and to make use of similar approaches when designing and making
	aim for a high quality of accuracy and presentation
	consider the influence of advertising on consumers
	understand how market research can be used to measure user needs and market potential

Supermarkets are convenient because they are local, easily accessible, have plenty of parking space and sell a wide range of foods in one shop. They also have competitive prices because they are part of a large chain.

Small supermarkets have cheap foods but less choice than the larger ones. Market stalls may have even cheaper foods, but often you are unable to pick out the food yourself.

Specialist shops, such as butchers, bakers, greengrocers and fishmongers, have a wide selection of their particular food. They are able to give the customer personal service, expert advice and foods at competitive prices.

The most expensive grocery shop tends to be the local corner shop. They have a limited range of stock, but they are convenient because they are nearby and have long opening hours.

Fig. 5.56

Supermarket design

About half of all food shopping is bought from the main supermarket chains. Each chain has an image which is recognisable in each of its supermarkets. It includes the design and layout of the store, own-brand labels, price labels, carrier bags, and even the uniform worn by the staff. The aim of this image is to promote loyalty to the chain, and to encourage customers to go into one of their supermarkets even if it is in an unfamiliar area.

All supermarkets use various methods to encourage customers to buy their goods. As soon as you enter the supermarket you see advertisements for different foods making your mouth water and tempting you to start buying immediately. The trolleys are large (and getting larger) so it is difficult to judge how much shopping you have in them. The lighting and mirrors make the supermarket look bright and welcoming and certain foods, especially fruit and vegetables, look fresh and appetizing.

All supermarkets have long aisles. Everyday goods that are in high demand are displayed in the middle of the aisles or at the back of the supermarket. Customers regularly come in for these goods, but to find them, they may have to search long shelves of other goods, which the supermarket hopes they will be tempted to buy as well. Every so often a supermarket may rearrange all the goods to bring different items to the attention of customers.

Technology

Computers play a large part in the operating of a modern supermarket. They control records of stock, read bar codes on goods and order replacement stock when necessary. Foods no longer have to be individually price tagged. A laser scanner, attached to a computerised cash register, reads the bar code and sends the information to a computer terminal. The description and price is sent back to the check-out and is printed on the till receipt. All goods have their own bar code for easy identification.

EXTRAS

1. Visit your local supermarket and make a list of the various methods it uses to encourage you to **(a)** enter the supermarket and **(b)** buy more goods.

6 BUSINESS & ECONOMICS

In your Design & Technology activities, you will work in two main ways – either on your own or with other people. A successful activity often depends upon teamwork and cooperation. Successful groups such as Dire Straits, or teams such as Nottingham Forest, would probably agree that their success is the result of teamwork. The same is true of large businesses, such as Shell, Unilever and Rolls Royce.

Business and industry

Business and industry involves the whole process of manufacturing and trading, including financial services. Businesses produce **goods** or **services**. These are offered to the public, who are known as **consumers**.

Everyone is a consumer – everyone buys food and clothes, gets their video, bicycle or car repaired, and expects water, electricity and gas to be available when they want it.

Business is part of everyone's life. Have you noticed how many news items on television or in the newspapers are connected with business and industry?

Fig. 6.1 Everyone benefits from working with other people

New effort to cut cost of fitness

River site on hold until office rents pick up

MAJOR multi-million

By NIGEL SMITH

Cab plan hailed

MINICABS could face strict new laws if recommendations for unlicensed taxis get the go-ahead.

The Labour controlled Association of London Authorities decided last week to endorse a two-tier system of licensing all London taxis.

The decision pre-empts a working party report, commissioned by

Unlike minicab drivers, the black cab drivers are monitored by the Public Carriage Office and are subject to strict checks on their cars, health and passing the infamous Knowledge road test. Many minicab firms have welcomed the recommendations. Michael Main, quality controller of Greater London Hire, said:

Fig. 6.2 Business is all around you

	In D&T, you will learn to:
	devise an effective strategy for investigating a specific situation
	recognise that the preferences of consumers can change
	recognise the relationship between price, cost, income and competition in the market for goods and services

The economy

Britain has what is known as a **mixed economy**. This means that the production of goods and services is controlled by both the Government and **private producers** (organisations that produce goods or services). These include businesses set up by individuals, partnerships, or groups of people such as Marks & Spencer and Woolworth. Industries run by the Government are known as **nationalised** industries, for example the Post Office.

During the 1980s, many nationalised industries such as British Gas, British Aerospace, British Airways and British Telecom were **privatised**. This means that each industry was put up for sale, and private investors bought **shares** in the organisation so that they owned part of it.

Goods and services

There are three stages in producing goods and services:

1 primary production is concerned with extracting natural resources, for example fishing, agriculture, mining and forestry;

2 secondary production involves using raw materials to manufacture and assemble goods, for example food, drink, cars and videos;

3 tertiary production is concerned with the production of services, for example banking, insurance, retailing, entertainment, hairdressing, health and education.

Specialisation

The economy is based on **specialisation**, which means that people usually specialise in producing one particular type of goods or service – for example, a farmer specialises in producing food and a plumber specialises in installing and servicing waterpipes. As people do not produce all the things they need, they rely on other people. In the same way, businesses depend on one another. If the sheep farmer did not rear and shear the sheep, the mills would have no wool to make the jumpers, and there would be nothing for the shop to sell.

Making a profit

Commercial companies are in business to make a **profit**. They have to provide goods or services that people want, otherwise they will go out of business. Their financial plans need to be worked out very carefully. If a firm is to stay in business it has to be sure that the money it will receive for its goods and services – its **revenue** – is more than the amount that it has to pay out – its **costs**. The things that businesses need to consider when arranging their finances are looked at in more detail on pages 114–119. As long as the total revenue is greater than the total costs, then the firm is making a profit and can carry on in business.

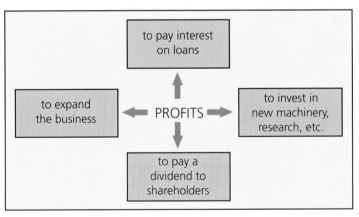

Fig. 6.4 Using profits

Non profit-making organisations

Charitable organisations, such as the Citizen's Advice Bureau and the Royal Society for the Prevention of Cruelty to Animals, and consumer organisations also offer a service to the public. They do not get paid for their services. In order to remain in operation, they organise fund-raising events and make bids for official grants. Such organisations need to work out their financial and marketing plans carefully.

Fig. 6.3 One business depends on another

Responding to change

Businesses have to cope with constant changes, such as the following:

- new products which are launched by other businesses
- the changing tastes of consumers
- changes in the population
- social changes
- new laws affecting their particular business
- competition from other countries
- new developments in technology.

EXTRAS

1. Choose a local company and investigate the possible effects of its closure, or the relocation of its business to another area of the country. You could consider things like the loss of jobs, the effect upon other local businesses, the cost of social security and redundancy payments, and the loss of competition for other businesses.

2. Businesses must respond to changes in the market for their goods (seven suggested changes are listed in the 'Responding to change' section above). Using a local business as an example, carry out research to find out more about the effects of at least one of these changes on the business.

Basic Needs and Wants

Fig. 6.5a Are my needs …

People have basic needs – air, water, food, warmth, shelter and clothing. Once these are satisfied, it would probably be more accurate to label other 'needs' as 'wants'. How often have you said, 'I need a new pair of trainers' or some other item? Do you *need* them or do you *want* them? What might be seen in Britain as a necessity, for example a cooker, might be seen as a luxury in other parts of the world. Wants are satisfied by buying goods and using services. Look at Figs. 6.5a and b. What do they tell you about human needs and wants?

Fig. 6.5b … the same as hers?

Resources

Resources which are used to produce goods and services can be divided into three main categories:

1 land, coal, iron ore, tin and oil which are known as **natural resources**;

2 labour, both physical and mental, which is known as the **human resource**;

3 machinery, equipment, factories, transportation systems and finance are usually referred to as **capital resources**.

Every country in the world has to cope with the problem of scarcity of resources. There is only a limited supply of resources available, and there are not enough resources to satisfy everyone's needs. People can only produce a certain number of goods or services over a particular period of time, but there seem to be

Fig. 6.6 Resources are limited

	In D&T, you will learn to:
	investigate the effects of design and technological activity on the environment, and take account of its impact
	recognise potential conflicts between the needs of individuals and of society
	recognise that a solution may result in problems in other areas

no limits to the goods or services that people want to consume.

Countries at different stages of economic development have different levels of resources. If you lived in an under-developed area, such as parts of India or Africa, there would be fewer resources available to you than there are in this country. Britain does not have many natural resources but it is strong in skills and capital (money). Britain has adopted new technology, and people's wants have changed in line with these technological changes. Britain cannot produce all that is needed to satisfy consumers' wants, so what

cannot be made is imported. Goods, such as electrical equipment, are imported from Japan, and foods that cannot be grown successfully in this country, such as melons, grapefruit and oranges, are also imported.

Nowadays, most families in Britain have a television or a car. These are often regarded as necessities. Such items were considered to be luxuries 30 years ago.

People's wants are **interdependent**. For example, when someone buys a car, this in turn creates other wants – petrol, oil, spare parts and a parking space.

Opportunity cost

Businesses use up resources that are scarce. Once a resource has been used for one purpose, it cannot be used for anything else. The decision to have one thing rather than another has an **opportunity cost** in terms of what has been done without. For example, if you decide to spend your pocket money on a new CD you lose the opportunity to spend that money on something else, such as ice-skating or a new T-shirt.

Fig. 6.7 Decisions! Decisions!

Choices

The use of resources needs to be considered very carefully, whether they are natural resources, such as land or oil, or human resources – people and their skills. The alternative choices available must be looked at, and a decision made as to which choice is best and why. A piece of land could be used for a number of purposes, but using it for one of these purposes prevents it from being used for any other purpose (see Fig. 6.8). You will need to make similar choices in your Design & Technology activities when you decide which materials to use, and how best to use your time.

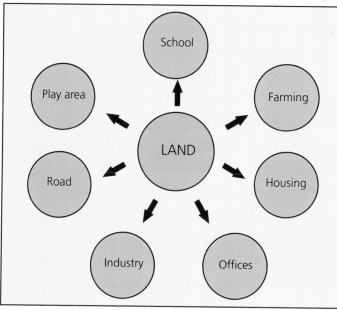

Fig. 6.8 Land can be used for different purposes

Costs and benefits

When you have to consider alternative solutions to a problem, you might ask yourself 'Who or what are the winners, and who or what are the losers?' What are the advantages and the disadvantages of the alternative solutions? Business activities result in both **costs** and **benefits** to individuals and to society. Consider the costs and benefits of locating a new factory on farmland on the edge of a local village:

Benefits

- profits for owners of the new factory
- creation of jobs for local people
- more money brought into the area
- increased business for suppliers

Costs

- pollution (air, noise, water)
- spoilt views for some residents
- loss of farmland and produce
- damage to natural habitat – plants and wildlife

EXTRAS

1. Write down the costs and benefits of locating a major airport in a local rural area.

2. In a group, discuss whether it is better to produce electricity by nuclear power rather than by burning coal.

Business Management

How is your school organised? Your school is an organisation which provides a service – your education – and it should be run efficiently. Responsibility for running a school on a day-to-day basis usually lies with the headteacher and senior management – the deputy heads or senior teachers. How does this compare with the organisational structure of your school?

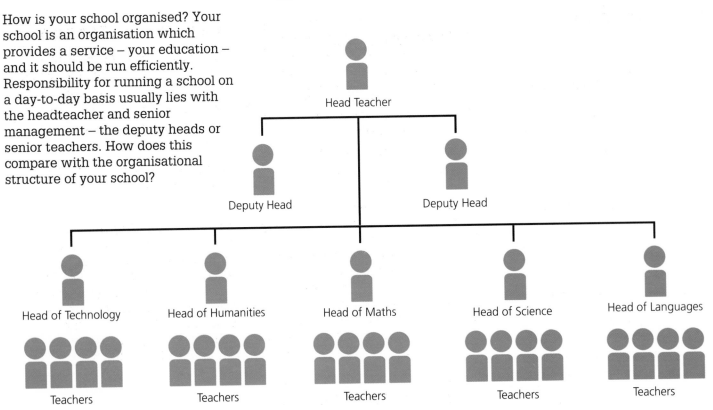

Fig. 6.9 A typical organisation chart for a secondary school

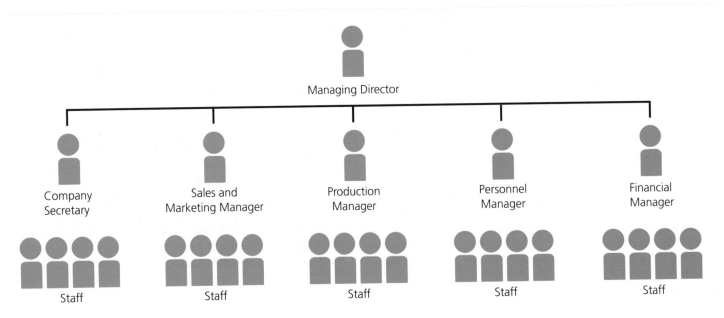

Fig. 6.10 A typical organisation chart for a business

In D&T, you will learn to:
realise that, when working in teams, people may have specialist roles
recognise that people are an important resource and need to be trained, organised and motivated
recognise and represent organisational structures

In small businesses, a single owner may be responsible for all the functions of management. He/she will have to make all the decisions. In larger organisations, the business is likely to be split into departments. Fig. 6.10 shows one example of how a company might structure its management.

Situations vacant

Sales and Marketing Manager

Creativity and imagination are two of the qualities we are looking for in this post. We need someone who can work on his/her own initiative to promote and sell our existing products. You would also need to be able to spot opportunities for new product lines.

Large companies may have separate departments for **Sales** and **Marketing**. The **Marketing Department** carries out market research (see pages 104–105) and handles the promotion and advertising of the range of products. New products will need to be researched and developed in order for the company to stay competitive and cater for any changes in the tastes of consumers. The **Sales Department** forms the link between the company and the consumer. Sales representatives sell the company's goods or services, and may build up a close relationship with a network of customers. The salesforce will pass vital information on to the Marketing staff.

Company Secretary

If you are hardworking, methodical, and have an eye for detail then read on. We need a Company Secretary who will ensure that both internal and external communications are correctly and efficiently maintained. Secretarial and administrative staff are available to support the successful candidate.

The **Company Secretary** has responsibility for a business's legal affairs and administration. In addition to organising a company's offices and methods of communications, he/she will also keep shareholders fully informed about financial aspects of the company. The Company Secretary will make arrangements for Board Meetings – arranging the agenda, minutes of meetings and all relevant correspondence.

Managing Director

We need a leader, someone with drive and enthusiasm who is receptive to new ideas, yet can make decisions and act upon them.

Do you fit the bill?

The **Managing Director** (MD) is rather like a head teacher in a school. He/she leads the organisation, supported by specialist managers. The MD makes important decisions and although he/she can take the credit for successful trading, he/she also has to take much of the blame for poor company performance. It can be very tough at the top.

FINANCIAL MANAGER

We need someone with an aptitude for figures – someone who is honest and reliable, can balance our books and prepare reports. Have you got the necessary accountancy experience and/or qualifications?

The **Finance Department** looks after all the money coming in and going out of the company. This will involve paying for wages, materials and machinery – expenses incurred in producing the goods or services. The Finance Department may also be responsible for issuing invoices to customers for goods or services provided.

PRODUCTION MANAGER

Our production line is equipped with the latest technology. Would you like to be responsible for scheduling its use and ensuring that we do not waste either time or materials?

A team of skilled workers awaits your leadership.

The **Production Department** is responsible for changing raw materials into finished products. Adequate supplies of materials must be available at the required time in order to maintain levels of production. Equipment must be maintained in good working order, and the workforce has to be organised.

Personnel Manager

Can you promote teamwork? Are you interested in looking after the training and welfare of others? If you feel you are able to communicate and negotiate with people at all levels, you could be the person we are looking for.

The **Personnel Department** is responsible for recruiting the right person for the right job. They also organise staff training, promotions, wages, sickness benefit, holiday pay and pensions. In addition, they conduct negotiations with trade unions with regard to issues such as health and safety, working conditions and dismissals.

EXTRAS

1. You might like to consider which of the positions described on this page appeals to you most. Have you the right qualities? Have you any relevant experience? What kind of further training/qualifications would you need?

2. Work out a structure for the organisation of a school-based business. What roles will be needed and what will be each role's main area of responsibility?

Marketing

Marketing is about making sure that people want to buy what you are selling, and making sure that you are producing what people want to buy – that you are satisfying a need. Selling a product is not as simple as it might seem. Serious thought has to be given to how the product will be advertised, where it will be sold and what it will cost.

The marketing mix

The things which have to be thought about when selling a product are usually referred to as the **marketing mix**. Thinking of this as the '4 Ps' will make it easy to remember. Fig. 6.11 shows the marketing mix and explains what is meant by the '4 Ps'.

Fig. 6.11 The marketing mix

Marketing Checklist
Fig. 6.12

- Conduct market research on your product to find out whether it is what consumers want (see pages 104 –105).

- Consider how to promote your product to make sure there is a demand for it. Decide where to advertise and which sales promotion techniques you will use.

- Decide what price to charge, taking competitors' prices into consideration.

- Consider how to distribute your product and where it will be sold.

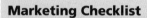

In D & T, you will learn to:
test simple objects you have made
propose modifications to improve the performance and appeal of existing products
know that aesthetic qualities influence consumers' choices
recognise that the preferences of consumers can change
know that original designs can be granted patents
recognise the relationship between price, cost, income and competition in the market for goods and services

Case Study – the Wispa bar

When Cadbury's development team designed a new textured chocolate bar they had some important decisions to make. These decisions were concerned with the marketing mix.

Product
They experimented with many different shapes of chocolate bar and tested them on groups of consumers before deciding on the final design. Many different names were considered before the name 'Wispa' was finally chosen. The distinctive blue and red wrapper was decided upon to give the bar the image the designers wanted – a stylish, modern bar of good quality.

Price
Cadbury's looked carefully at prices charged by their competitors and decided to charge 17p for Wispa bars. At the time this was 1p less than a Mars bar and 1p more than an Aero.

Promotion
Wispa bars were sold in the Newcastle-on-Tyne area before being advertised throughout the country. The bars were so successful that three months' production was sold in a single day. A £7.5 million advertising campaign followed, using television, press, posters, money-off coupons, etc. The Wispa bar is now the best-selling all-chocolate bar. If all the Wispa bars sold since its launch were laid end-to-end, they would stretch almost three times round the world.

Place
Wispa bars were sold in supermarkets, sweet shops, etc, and 80 extra salespeople had to be taken on to make sure that the product was available in the shops.

The lifecycle of a product

Consumers' tastes are always changing. In order for a business to be successful the directors must be aware of these changes, and also try to guess what the consumer is likely to want in the future. Otherwise, goods will be produced that no one wants to buy, causing sales and profits to fall.

As new goods and services come on to the market they affect the sales of goods which are already available. Every product has a lifespan during which demand for the product changes. The introduction of a new product is expensive as it has to be promoted through advertising. Until it has been on sale for a while, the company is unlikely to make much profit. As people get to know about the product the number of sales will increase, and the marketing managers may want to spend less money on advertising. Eventually, sales will reach a peak, or maturity, which means that sales are at their best. Finally, following a period where sales level off there is likely to be a decline in sales as consumers lose interest in the product. The company may well decide that it is not worth manufacturing the product any more. The length of this lifespan will vary from product to product. Some products are affected by changing fashions, and soon become out of date. Clothes, for example, have a short lifespan. Other products may be popular for much longer – for example, the Citroen 2CV, shown in Fig. 6.14, was a popular car for over 40 years. The decision to stop making it caused complaints from many of its fans.

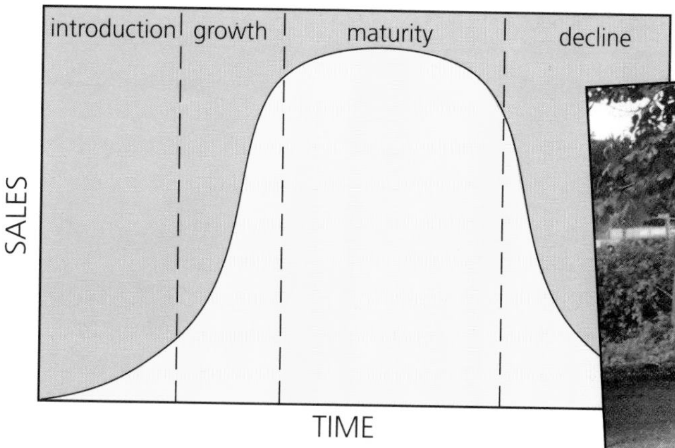

Fig. 6.13 Graph showing the lifecycle of a product

Fig. 6.14 The Citroen 2CV

Research and development

A successful company will develop new products as well as making changes to the old ones. This may be the job of the Marketing Department, or in large companies, there may be a **Research and Development Department**. They will use the information given to them by the Marketing Department to design and develop new products which are more attractive to the consumer.

Prototypes and patents

Once a design has been developed, a **prototype** is built and tested. It is usual for various prototypes to be built, tested, evaluated and modified until a successful product is achieved.

If the new product is different from others on the market, the company will want to protect their idea and prevent it from being copied. In Britain, this is done by applying to the Government Patent Office for a **patent**. This will prevent other companies from using the idea for up to 20 years, without the permission of the owner of the patent. Applying for a patent can be a long and costly process, and a smaller company may decide not to apply for one. Instead they may aim to sell large quantities of their product at a competitive price before other companies are able to copy their idea.

Fig. 6.15 Probe III, the Ford Sierra prototype

Planned obsolescence

Designers may want their products to last only for a limited time, so that their customers have to buy more of them. Many motor cars are built to last only a certain number of years. This is known as **planned obsolescence**. Some manufacturers, however, believe that they will gain more customers overall by making products that last. In a recent sales promotion, Volvo claimed that their cars are planned to last for nearly 20 years. As a result, half of all Volvos ever built are still on the road.

Market Research

Fig. 6.16 True or false?

How do you know whether what the people in Fig. 6.16 are saying is true or not? They are looking at the results of **market research** surveys. A number of people were asked questions on a particular subject. The market researchers then studied their answers and came to some conclusions.

Fig. 6.17 Craftspeople at work in the eighteenth century

What is market research?

Market research involves collecting information from people, recording it and making sense of it. It is carried out for two main reasons - to find out the demand for goods or services, and to find out what will persuade people to buy or use them.

Less than two hundred years ago, there was no need for market research because there were close links between consumers and producers. Craftspeople produced goods within small communities until the Industrial Revolution. Large quantities of goods could then be made by machinery instead of by hand, and firms could begin to meet the demands of consumers who lived outside their immediate area. Market research was needed to help the firms find out where their goods were wanted.

Market research helps people involved in business to plan rather than to guess. You cannot just hope that your product will be popular with other people, you need to find out if this will be the case.

Carrying out market research

Specialist marketing people usually carry out market research and this can be expensive. Anyone can carry out a survey or an investigation, but this may be worthless as it may only show what the 'researcher' wants to prove. For example, a market research survey may claim that

'80 per cent of youngsters prefer classical music'. When you question these findings, you may discover that the researchers only surveyed 20 youngsters; that they were all members of a local orchestra; and that the questions they were asked were based on a choice of either classical music or top 20 records, and omitted the wide range of music in between.

Market research surveys should include a reasonable cross-section of the people relevant to the survey. The researcher mentioned above should have interviewed youngsters from a range of backgrounds and interests, in order to obtain a representative view of youngsters' musical tastes. You can obtain useful information for your Design & Technology activities if you carry out your market research as the professionals do (see Fig. 6.18).

In D & T, you will learn to:
know that aesthetic qualities influence consumers' choices
identify markets for goods and services and recognise local variations in demand
know that advertising helps promote and sell goods and services
understand how market research can be used to measure user needs and market potential

Market Research Checklist

Before you can successfully market your goods or services, you will need to consider these questions:

- Who is the target market for your product? (Who are you going to sell it to? You need to consider their age, sex, social background and the region of the country where they live.)

- Is your sample group of people representative of the target market? (Are you surveying the right cross-section of people?)

- What do people want? What do they like or dislike about a product – its design, quality, colour, etc?

- What is the competition for your product?

- How are you going to collect your information?

Fig. 6.18

Collecting information

There are a number of different methods of market research. These are shown in Fig. 6.19. **Field Research** (primary information) involves collecting information first-hand – interviews, questionnaires and consumer tests (when a product is sampled). **Desk Research** (secondary information) involves using information which has already been collected by someone else – opinion polls, official statistics and company and trade reports.

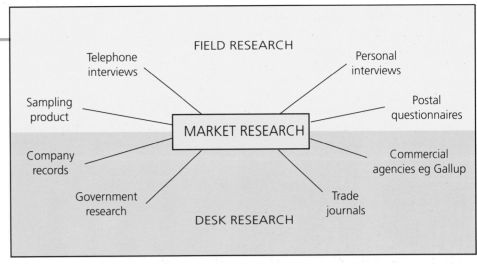

Fig. 6.19 A variety of approaches to market research

Questionnaires

Questionnaires are the most popular method of collecting primary information, but care should be taken when planning them. Questions should be *clear* and *easy to understand*. You need to ensure that your questions will provide the information you need.

Questionnaires use two types of question:

1 A **closed** question requires a one-word answer. You are often given several alternative answers from which to choose, for example, 'Which kind of music do you prefer – soul, top 20, classical, heavy rock, house, rap, reggae, thrash?' Closed questions are used when you need to count the number of answers for one topic, and when you are looking for specific information.

2 An **open** question requires a more detailed answer, for example, 'Who is your favourite group and why do you like them?' Open questions ask for more general information, and invite people to say why they prefer something. They allow people to say what they feel in their own words.

Most well-constructed questionnaires contain a combination of both open and closed questions.

Interviews

A structured interview, based on a questionnaire, may be conducted face-to-face or over the telephone. An in-depth interview is more likely to be conducted personally, and would be used to find out about people's attitudes to new products before they are tried out on the general public.

Fig. 6.20

Sampling

You may select a sample group of people for your market research. The group may be selected at random – pure chance as to who is selected to answer your questions – or it may be targeted – a specific number of people of a particular age, or from a particular region of the country.

It may be desirable to 'test' your product on such a group, as Cadbury's did when they 'test launched' Wispa bars in the north-east of England (see page 102).

EXTRAS

1. Try out a range of market research techniques. Which method was most effective and why? Would different methods suit different situations? What factors determine the choice of method to be used?

2. There are varying demands for some products in different regions of the country. Why do you think this is so?

Advertising your Goods or Services

Advertising has two main purposes:

1 to **inform** – let people know about your goods or services;
2 to **persuade** – encourage people to buy your goods or services rather than somebody else's.

Advertising can change consumer tastes. For instance, young people can be persuaded to buy an energy drink, such as Lucozade, that was previously thought suitable only for those who were ill.

Most advertising is designed simply to increase a company's **market share**. This means that two companies sell similar products, but one company sells more of its products than the other and, therefore, has a larger share of the market. Washing powder advertisements do not make people wash their clothes more. However, each of the two main washing powder companies spends millions of pounds trying to persuade people to use their particular powders rather than the other company's powders.

Fig. 6.21 Advertising media

Brands

Many firms aim to develop a strong brand image for their product to give it a distinct identity from other similar products. By advertising it widely, the firm hopes people will continue to buy it. Fig. 6.22 shows brands made by Nestlé.

Fig. 6.22 Nestlé Brands

In D&T, you will learn to:
use factual information and value judgements
recognise objective and subjective information
recognise that economic, moral and environmental factors can influence design and technological activities
consider the influence of advertising on consumers
know that advertising helps promote and sell goods and services.

Slogans

Do the following slogans sound familiar: 'Feed me now', 'Gotta Lotta Bottle', 'I know a man who can', and 'Everything we do is driven by you'? In which advertisements are they used? Advertisers use short, catchy, easy-to-remember slogans. Some are humorous and some use rhyme – it's all part of grabbing your attention.

Fig. 6.23 'Soft, strong and very, very long'

Logos

How many of the logos shown below do you recognise? Some products have such well-known logos that it is possible to advertise them without using words. Many companies employ **advertising agencies** to invent slogans, logos and advertising campaigns for them.

Advertising is money

Millions of pounds are spent on advertising every year by the big companies. The table in Fig. 6.24 shows the amount spent by some of the big names during 1988. One large manufacturer pointed out, 'Half the money we spend on advertising is money wasted. The trouble is, we don't know which half.' Is advertising a product money well spent? The companies seem to think so. They say that the extra sales of the product made as a result of advertising it more than pays for the cost of the advertising.

Name	Amount spent (£)	TV (%)	Press (%)	Other (%)	Examples of products
1 Proctor & Gamble	44,000,000	93	1	6	Ariel, Bold, Bounce, Pampers
2 Kelloggs	38,000,000	94	5	1	Cornflakes, All Bran, Rice Krispies,
3 Nestlé	32,000,000	70	26	4	Nescafé coffee, Waistline salad cream
4 Ford Motor Company	31,000,000	37	60	3	Escort, Sierra, vans
5 Austin Rover	31,000,000	67	31	2	Maestro, Metro, Rover
6 Electricity Council	30,000,000	57	41	2	Central heating, cookers
7 British Telecom	30,000,000	60	36	4	Yellow pages, residential calls
8 Gallaher Tobacco	27,000,000	7	93	0	Benson & Hedges cigarettes, Manikin cigars
9 Pedigree petfoods	27,000,000	91	7	2	Kit-e-Kat, Pal, Chum, Whiskas
10 Elida Gibbs	24,000,000	81	18	1	Timotei shampoo, Sunsilk shampoo, Impulse body spray

Fig. 6.24 Advertising is big business!

So mild you can wash your hair as often as you like.

As mild as only nature can be – Timotei shampoo. Timotei is mild both to your hair and to your scalp. It cleans your hair gently, leaving it soft and shiny with a fresh smell of summer meadows.

Timotei Shampoo.

Childhood diseases haven't died. Children have.

It's sad, but true. Childhood diseases like Mumps, Measles, Rubella, Diphtheria, Tetanus, Polio and Whooping Cough can all have very serious consequences.

They can lead to blindness, deafness, paralysis, brain damage and even death.

Rubella can be especially serious for a pregnant woman,

whose unborn child may be born deaf, blind or even brain damaged.

However, children don't have to be at risk.

Immunisation can protect against all these diseases and help to wipe them out.

So parents who don't immunise their children are taking needless risks.

The time to start your child's Immunisation programme is at the age of two months.

For more information and advice see your doctor or health visitor or just pop down to your local clinic.

They're there to help.

Remember, it's better for you to see your doctor before your child has to.

IMMUNISATION The safest way to protect your child.

Fig. 6.25 Different types of effective advertising

Effective advertising

Words and pictures must be chosen very carefully in order to attract and influence people. **Informative** advertising is often used by politicians to promote their views, for example the privatisation of public industries or health and safety issues. Organisers of events use informative advertising, otherwise no one would know the event was taking place. **Persuasive** advertising is used by companies to imply that people will benefit from the product, and a variety of images is used to get the message across: romance and sex appeal; keeping up with the Joneses; an improved standard of living; caring for the family; respect for the experts; hero worship; saving the environment; …you may be able to think of more.

Each type of advertising has its own price. For example, a 30-second advertisement during peak-time viewing on television costs about £20,000 and a full-page advertisement in *The Times* newspaper costs £15,000.

EXTRAS

1. Collect a range of newspaper and magazine advertisements and look at them with a critical eye. Sort them into groups according to the image being presented, for example, romance, hero worship, etc. Assess the text – is it short and simple, or longer and more informative?

2. Compare the costs of using different advertising media, for example, a 60-second slot on television; a 60-second slot on local radio; the cost per word in a newspaper or magazine; and the cost of advertising leaflets, per 1000 leaflets. The Advertising Association produces useful guides such as *Facts and Figures on Advertising*. Your local library may also have copies of publications such as *Campaign* and the current *AA Advertising Statistics Yearbook*.

Planning the message

'A picture is worth a thousand words' you are often told. 'It depends upon the picture' you might say. Notice how the impact is created in the advertisement shown in Fig. 6.26. Good design, planning and the careful choice of language are the skills needed to produce effective advertising material. You could collect other examples of effective advertisements which rely mainly on colour and graphics for their impact.

The drawings in Fig. 6.27 are taken from an East Midlands Electricity promotion which uses Brian Clough as the main character in its television advertisements. Once the advertising story has been written, an advertising studio will set out a rough version of the pictures and words to be used which are known as **storyboards**. These are pre-tested on members of the public before the advertisement is filmed.

Fig. 6.26 The picture says it all!

Alfonso, my new goalkeeper, finds it rather chilly here after Italy

So I got him a storage heating system from the team you can trust … East Midlands Electricity

Storage heating starts at around £200 … and runs on Economy 7 Electricity at less than half the price!

So, unlike Alfonso, it's very affordable

Gonna be hot stuff on Saturday Alfie?

(crash of plates smashing)

East Midlands Electricity …

… the team you can trust

Fig. 6.27 Storyboards from the East Midlands Electricity advertising campaign

In D&T, you will learn to:
recognise objective and subjective information
collate, sort, analyse, interpret and present information in a form appropriate to the purpose and the intended audience
develop styles of visual communication which take account of what is to be conveyed, the audience and the medium to be used
consider the influence of advertising on consumers
calculate costs and make decisions on price

Planning your Campaign Checklist   Fig. 6.28

1 Conduct market research to find out what people like; who will buy your product; how much they will pay, and where it will be sold.

2 Create the image, product name, and packaging, etc.

3 Find out how much money is available for your campaign.

4 Choose the media to reach your target audience.

5 Design your material, carefully considering the language and graphics to be used.

6 Arrange the test launch – the sampling of your goods or services.

7 Launch your product and be ready to meet the orders for it.

Packaging

The packaging of a product is important for creating the right image. Would you be tempted to buy products packaged in plain brown paper? Plastics, paper, board, aluminium, tin plate and glass are the main materials used in the packaging industry. How many different kinds of packaging material can you find in your home? Packaging has other functions apart from advertising the product. It gives the consumer information about the product – for example, its weight, the ingredients and the sell-by date. It also preserves and protects.

Fig. 6.29

In a group, discuss whether vast sums of money should be spent on advertising. You could consider the following statements in favour of advertising:

● it tells consumers about products
● it extends freedom of choice
● it entertains and is creative
● it pays for commercial television, papers and magazines.

In addition, consider the following statements against advertising:

● it creates unnecessary 'wants' and encourages people to overspend
● it creates envy and dissatisfaction
● it adds to the cost of goods;
● it trivialises human emotion
● it is wasteful and manipulates people.

Do you think that advertising reduces or increases competition between companies?

Protection for consumers

There are independent organisations which exist to protect consumers, often using laws passed by the Government:

● the Trade Descriptions Act 1968 ensures that what the advertisers claim about their products is accurate and truthful
● the Broadcasting Act 1981 controls advertisements on independent television and local radio. The Independent Broadcasting Authority ensures that advertisers comply with the code, and excludes any advertisement which would be likely to mislead people
● the British Code of Advertising Practice (BCAP) and the British Code of Sales Promotion Practice (BCSPP) provide control for all non-broadcast media
● the Advertising Standards Authority (ASA) investigates complaints about advertisements. Advertisers or agencies who have broken the Code find that the media will not accept their advertisements.

Fig. 6.30 The BCAP booklet and ASA brochures

EXTRAS

1. Design a poster or leaflet to be used for one of the following informative purposes:

to promote something you have made in Design & Technology; to promote the Channel Tunnel; to outline the dangers of smoking; or to publicise a political party founded by yourself.

2. Design your own television advertisement in the form of storyboards. Remember to consider your target audience, the image you wish to present, the message in terms of language and graphics, and the cost of it all. Perhaps you can arrange to video your planned advertisement.

Production

Production is the process of changing resources into goods and services which satisfy people's needs. It involves using raw materials and/or labour to make finished products or provide services which can be sold to the consumer. It is as much about the bus driver who offers you a service by driving you to school as it is about the person working on a car assembly line. Production adds value to something to turn it into goods or services that consumers will purchase.

During the last 10 years, whilst jobs in **manufacturing** have been declining, jobs in the **service** industries (finance, catering, tourism, leisure) have increased. Why do you think this is the case? Modern businesses and industries must be well organised in order to produce their goods and services efficiently, otherwise they may go out of business.

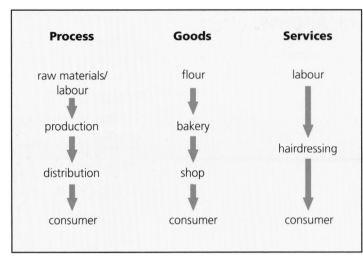

Fig. 6.31 A chain of production

Fig. 6.32 A design team's recommendations

The design team

The idea for a particular product or service may come from the Marketing Department because market research has shown that it is required, and there is little or no competition for it. Once it has been established that there is a market for the product or service, the **design team** produces a specification. This gives a list of the criteria that the product or service should satisfy. In the case of goods, it will also include their size, colour and the types of materials to be used. Designers have to make choices about materials, bearing in mind their suitability, cost and availability. There will be close cooperation between the design team and the Production Department while the various materials, equipment and production methods are investigated.

Prototypes are made and tested before large-scale production takes place (see the section on Marketing on pages 102–103). For example, a new ice cream bar would be pre-tested in selected areas of the country before being sold countrywide.

Job production

There are several different methods of producing goods and services. **Job production** involves producing 'one-off' products, for example individually designed clothing, individual hairstyling, landscape gardening and the construction of the Humber Bridge. Every item produced is different and, in some cases, a firm might have to rearrange its production floor to meet the special requirements of each job. Job production needs more labour than machines – it is **labour intensive**.

	In D & T, you will learn to:
	combine materials to create others with enhanced properties
	select a match of materials and equipment to create a quality outcome
	identify and use machines to perform tasks required by your design activities

Batch production

Batch production involves groups of similar items being produced at the same time, for example a range of bakery products or modern furniture (see Fig. 6.33).

Fig. 6.34

Mass production

Mass production is the production of goods and services on a very large scale. Vast numbers of identical products are made as cheaply as possible. This is known as the economy of large-scale production, or **economy of scale** for short. Mass production needs more machines than labour – some production lines are fully automated and only require 'machine minders' (see Fig.6.35).

Flow production

Flow production involves the products in passing through a number of stages with each stage adding to the product. Sweets, cars and computers are produced in this way (see Fig. 6.34).

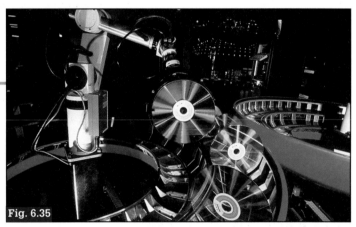
Fig. 6.35

Quality control

Quality control ensures that a product or service reaches a certain standard. This is important, as faulty goods can mean lower profits for the company. Quality control helps to ensure that the customer is satisfied with the product or service. There are two main factors:

1 Does the product or service satisfy the criteria of the specification?

2 Does the product or service meet official standards, for example, safety standards and the standards of the British Standards Institute?

You will ask yourself the first question during a Design & Technology activity. While making your product, you will refer to the specification and evaluate the product against it. You will probably also test the product, and ask other people's opinions on it. As a result, you may decide to modify the design of the product in order to improve it.

Division of labour

Modern manufacturing relies heavily on **division of labour** which means that each worker concentrates on doing one particular job. This is known as specialisation. You might like to think about the advantages and disadvantages of job specialisation. Producing goods involves a wide range of specialist and interdependent tasks. If Ford's engine plant at Bridgend went on strike, car production across Europe would stop!

EXTRAS

1. In a group, discuss the advantages and disadvantages of division of labour.

2. Visit a local firm to investigate their methods of production. Make a list of the specialist jobs in the firm. Then report your findings to the rest of the group.

Stock control

Before you start to make your Design & Technology product you should write lists of everything you will need to make it. This is called resource planning, and it is explained in *Design & Technology: The Process*. You may find that some items are not in stock in school, and will have to be ordered.

For businesses to be efficient, production lines need to operate most of the time. Therefore, planning has to be very good. A firm needs to make sure that it has enough resources – raw materials and components – to meet production plans. The Production Department must make sure that stocks are kept at the right level to avoid both understocking and overstocking – this is called **stock control**. Understocking could result in a firm running out of an important part or component which could mean the production line would stop. Overstocking costs money – stock has to be paid for, staff have to be paid to manage it, and stock may become out-of-date and, therefore, worthless. Stock levels are often monitored by computers. The people in charge of stock control decide what materials need to be kept in stock, how many of each item there should be, when an order for more materials should be placed, and how many of each item to order.

Case Study

Lena and Craig decided to produce a range of silk ties and scarves which they hoped to enter in a local craft competition. Their designs on paper were very impressive but, unfortunately, they had not checked the stock of silk paints and found out, too late, that their choice of colours was restricted to only two.

Make sure that this does not happen to you. You must plan your resources carefully beforehand. This includes the equipment you need to use. For example, if you need to use the computerised sewing machine three weeks into your project, you may need to book it in advance.

In D & T, you will learn to:
analyse the task and its components, to identify those which depend upon the completion of previous tasks, and to develop a flow chart
set objectives and identify resources and constraints
organise your working to complete the task on time
consider, when selecting and using materials, their physical and aesthetic properties, availability and cost, and the product being made
know that, in the production and distribution of goods, the control of stock is important

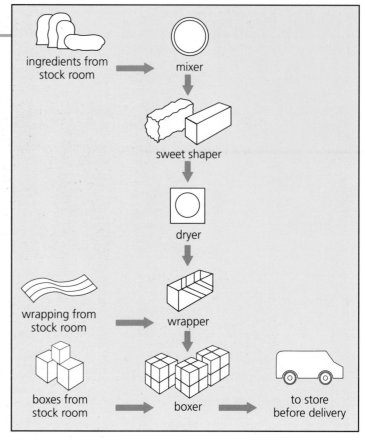

Fig. 6.36 A business production plan

Figure 6.37 shows a display of Thorntons' products. Thorntons is one of Britain's leading chocolate manufacturers. Fig. 6.38 shows Thorntons' staff producing sweets. Just imagine what might happen if they ran out of nuts – production could be halted, ingredients wasted, and output dramatically reduced. All in all, it would be a very costly mistake. Stock control staff make sure that this does not happen.

Fig. 6.37

Fig. 6.38

Fig. 6.39 From the producer to the consumer

Distribution

The role of **distribution** is to ensure that goods or services reach the right customer at the right time. Small firms, such as a smallholding (see Fig. 6.39) may sell produce direct to the consumer. However, large firms like Marks & Spencer have fleets of lorries to distribute goods direct from the manufacturer to retail outlets – their hundreds of branches. Traditionally, goods have been sold to wholesalers, who buy in bulk from manufacturers, and then sell the goods to retailers in smaller quantities.

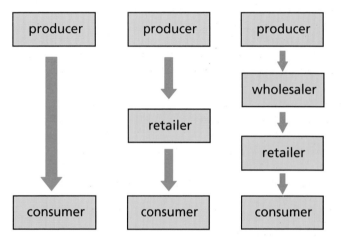

Fig. 6.40 Channels of distribution

Many services, such as banking, are sold direct to the customer. Building societies operate through their own branches, but also have 'agencies' at the offices of solicitors and estate agents. How many different types of retail outlet can you identify in Fig. 6.41?

Fig. 6.41

Production Checklist
Fig. 6.42

- Consider what materials and processes are available to you before deciding what product to make.

- Plan your resources in advance, ensuring that they will be available when you require them.

- Plan each stage of the production process in detail, bearing in mind any constraints.

- Consider whether there are any quality control measures which could be introduced.

- Evaluate your production process – could it be made more efficient?

Case Study

When Lena and Craig left school, they set up their own small business with the help of an enterprise grant. Although they hoped to be able to persuade some shops to take their goods, they also looked at other ways of distributing goods to consumers, such as through craft fairs and by mail order. Write down any other outlets available to them.

EXTRAS

1. a) Find out how stock is monitored and controlled in your school. You could begin by looking at the Design & Technology department.

b) Carry out research to find out how a local business controls its stock. Compare the two systems of stock control, and write down any improvements that you can suggest.

Costing and Pricing

Fig. 6.43 What shall we charge?

When deciding what price to charge for a product or service, businesses have to consider factors such as:

● how much it will cost to make the product or provide the service;
● how much needs to be added on in order to make a profit;
● whether people will pay that price.

The price has to be high enough to cover the costs of production and give a profit, but not so high that people will not buy the product or service. Market research can indicate whether people are prepared to pay a certain price. This method of fixing the price is known as a **cost plus** pricing policy.

Fixed and variable costs

Costs fall into two main categories:

1 fixed costs which include rent for premises, the cost of machinery, and administrative costs. These *stay the same*, no matter how many products are made;

2 variable costs which include raw materials, labour and energy. These *increase* as production increases.

The **total costs** can be worked out by adding the fixed costs and variable costs together (see Fig. 6.44).

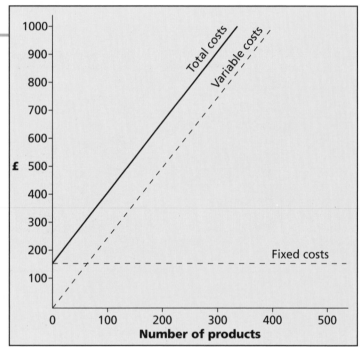

Fig. 6.44 Costs

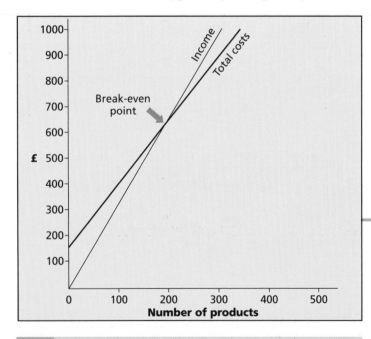

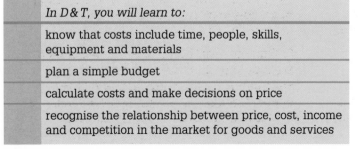

	In D & T, you will learn to:
	know that costs include time, people, skills, equipment and materials
	plan a simple budget
	calculate costs and make decisions on price
	recognise the relationship between price, cost, income and competition in the market for goods and services

The break-even point

The money received from selling a product or service is known as the **income** or **revenue**. The **break-even point** is the point at which the income is the same as the money being spent on fixed and variable costs (**expenditure**).

Fig. 6.45 The break-even point

Cash flow

Small businesses often collapse because they have not considered carefully enough the prices they need to charge in order to make a profit. There must be enough money coming in to pay the bills. If expenditure exceeds income for too long, the business will become **bankrupt**. The money coming in and going out of a business is known as the **cash flow**.

Personal budgeting

How is your cash flow situation? Do you manage your finances efficiently?

Helen decided to monitor the use of her money over a short period, so that she could work out how much she could save towards her skiing holiday in a few months' time. She kept a record of her income and expenditure over one month. By doing this, she worked out that she could save 75p a week towards her holiday. How much will she have saved during the 10 weeks before her holiday?

	A	B	C	D	E	F	G
1		My Budget					
2	Date	Income	£	Expenditure	£	Balance	Savings
3	10-May	Paper round	4.50	Magazine	0.75	3.75	
4				Mum's present	2.50	1.25	
5				Sweets	0.50	0.75	0.75
6							
7	17-May	Paper round	4.50	Magazine	0.75	3.75	
8				Cinema	3.00	0.75	
9				Sweets	0.25	0.50	0.50
10							
11	24-May	Paper round	4.50	Magazine	0.75	3.75	
12				Ice Skating	2.75	1.00	1.00
13							
14	31-May	Paper round	4.50	Magazine	0.75	3.75	
15				Book	3.00	0.75	0.75

Fig. 6.46 Budgeting on a spreadsheet

Case Study

Sarah and Richard decided to set up a car valeting service, and have found a small site in a local business park. They estimate that their total costs for the first month will be:

Fixed Costs

Rent of premises	£100
Wages	£400
Hire charges	£120
Advertising	£40
Telephone	£35
Sundries	£25

Variable Costs

Services	£30
Consumables	£30

They have estimated how long it will take to carry out the service they plan to offer, and they think that they can fit in 15 cars per day, allowing for lunch and tea breaks. They intend to work a 5-day week. Market research has shown that potential customers would be willing to pay £5 for the complete service – washing, waxing and vacuuming the car.

Fig. 6.47 shows Sarah and Richard's total costs, their estimated revenue and the break-even point. How many cars will they have to service before they begin to make a profit? As there will be a period of time before they make a profit, they will have to visit their bank manager to apply for a loan to cover this period.

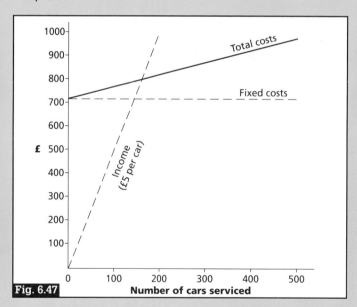

Fig. 6.47

Supply and demand

The **demand** for goods or services varies according to the amount consumers are willing to buy. Demand is influenced by price and other factors, such as changing consumer tastes in fashion and cars, and changes in trends, for example the current concern for caring for the environment. Can you think of any other factors that may affect the demand for goods or services?

The **supply** is the total amount of a particular product that a supplier can provide. Supply can be increased if manufacturers make more of the product, so supply normally follows demand.

EXTRAS

1. In a group, suggest what the fixed and variable costs would be for **a)** a hairdresser's, **b)** a food-processing plant, or **c)** an engineering firm.

2. Find out whether different types of labour are costed at different levels in your area. For example, what is the hourly rate for a window cleaner, a car mechanic, a machine operator, and an office supervisor, etc?

Business Plans

Anita Roddick, who set up The Body Shop by making the products at her home, was initially turned down by her bank manager when she requested a loan. She felt that he did not take her seriously. However, she returned smartly dressed, accompanied by her husband and, most importantly, with a detailed **business plan**. This time she was successful in getting the financial help she needed.

She has amazed critics by building up a very successful business while, at the same time, showing genuine concern for the environment. None of The Body Shop products are tested on animals, and only natural materials are used to make them. The packaging is kept to a minimum, the containers can be refilled, and promotional material is presented on recycled paper.

Fig. 6.48

Why do you need a business plan?

Before setting up in business, it is essential to carry out market research to find out whether people would be prepared to buy your goods or services, and the best way to tell them about it (see pages 104–109). Once you have established that there is a need, the next step is to prepare a business plan which sets out the financial needs of the business. This will help you to decide whether or not to go ahead with it. It will also provide you with the information you will need if you have to ask for a loan or an overdraft from the bank. Your business plan should contain a detailed examination of your product and the market, and a cash flow forecast for the first few months of trading.

Fig. 6.50 shows Sarah's and Richard's cash flow forecast for their car valeting business (see the case study on page 115).

A business plan enables both you and the bank to work out the level of risk that will be taken in setting up your business.

In D&T, you will learn to:
prepare a business plan, including a cash forecast and budget, and monitor performance against it
calculate costs and make decisions on price
recognise the relationship between price, cost, income and competition in the market for goods and services

Fig. 6.50	Jan	Feb	Mar	Apr	May	Jun
Balance		−115	−110	50	315	430
Income	**600**	**800**	**1000**	**1000**	**1000**	**1000**
Costs						
Rent	100	100	100	100	100	100
Wages	400	400	400	400	400	400
Services		70			150	
Telephone			105			105
Advertising	40	40	40	40	40	40
Hire charges	120	120	120	120	120	120
Consumables	30	40	50	50	50	50
Sundries	25	25	25	25	25	25
Total costs	**715**	**795**	**840**	**735**	**885**	**840**
Balance	**−115**	**−110**	**50**	**315**	**430**	**590**

Doing it yourself!

For at least some of your Design & Technology activities, you need to find out whether your design proposal would meet consumers' needs, and sell in sufficient quantities for you to make a healthy profit if you were to produce it for a business. To do this, you will need to do the following in the designing, planning and making stages of your project:

● carry out market research
● work out the costings for producing your goods or service
● prepare a detailed business plan (see Fig. 6.51)
● launch your goods or service
● compare your actual trading results with your estimated ones
● evaluate the success of your business venture considering what you would do differently if you could do it again.

What should the business plan include?

Your business plan should include the following details:

1 The **owner** – who you are, your background, the names of two referees.

2 The **business background** – the name of the business, its address, the main people involved in running it.

3 The **goods/service** – a detailed description of the goods or service.

4 The **market** – the details of market research you have carried out – prospective customers, major competitors, anticipated sales, proposed price/charge.

5 **Advertising and promotion** – your proposed methods for advertising and promoting the goods or service.

6 **Premises and equipment** – the possible locations for premises, including planning regulations if appropriate; the costs of premises and equipment; an investigation of available grants and your own cash resources.

7 **Cash flow** – a cash flow forecast showing details of expected income and expenditure during the first few months of trading.

8 **Financial requirements** – details of how much money needs to be borrowed from the bank.

9 **Future plans** – your plans for things such as increased production; new types of product; possible new competition.

Remember that your business plan should be well presented and can include photographs and illustrations.

Fig. 6.51

Our Products

We produce a wide range of modern, inexpensive jewellery, made from metal with enamelled decoration. We offer a selection of hand-made earrings, bracelets and necklaces.

Our Market

Market research has shown that there is a gap in the market locally for inexpensive unusual pieces of jewellery. Our target market is the 12 - 20 age group. Although our potential customers have limited spending powers, they purchase jewellery frequently. 75% of people questioned buy items of jewellery more than 3 times per month.

Advertising and Promotion

We have prepared flyers to give to pupils/parents/teachers at our school and posters to be displayed in the post office and local shops. A local hotel has agreed to allow us to use a display cabinet as we are donating 50% of our profits to a local charity. Our headteacher has agreed

Fig. 6.52 Part of a pupil's business plan

EXTRAS

1. Investigate the range of sources of finance available to a new business, such as using one's own savings, borrowing from family and friends, issuing shares in the business, government and private grants, and negotiating a loan or an overdraft with the bank. Which would be most appropriate to finance your Design & Technology enterprise?

2. Identify at least six business opportunities in your area and, following discussion, choose two that you think could be developed realistically. Give reasons for your choice.

Working Efficiently

Once you have identified a need, you will no doubt consider a number of design ideas before planning and making your chosen design. You may reject some ideas because of the cost, or difficulty of making them. Following the market research stage, designers in business go through the same process, often producing prototypes for sampling (see page 103) before deciding on the final design of the product.

Having decided what you are going to make, the next step is to plan carefully how you will make it. Whether you are making a one-off product or producing thousands of products, the things you need to consider are similar. Just as in business, you may have to work to tight deadlines and, therefore, it is essential that you plan the order of your work thoroughly. Fig. 6.53 shows the stages that you should work through in Design & Technology, and the stages that people in a business work through.

Design & Technology	Business
Opportunities for designing • identify needs and opportunities for designing • collect information by carrying out surveys using questionnaires, conducting interviews, or making your own observations • record your findings and any conclusions you have reached	• carry out market research on the proposed product • investigate competitors' products
Generating a design • identify any constraints for your product, such as materials, cost, time, size, etc • draw up a specification for your product • evaluate your ideas by modelling and testing them • choose one idea and modify it, if necessary, to form your design proposal	• plan how to market the product • plan how to finance the product • research and develop new products
Planning and making • plan the making of your product • order any materials or parts you will need, and book any specialised machinery you will need to use • allocate tasks to members of the team • make your product, modifying it if necessary, and record the making at each stage	• organise division of labour • consider stock control • decide on the type of production – job, batch, flow or mass production • ensure quality control
Evaluating • evaluate your product against the specification • ask other people to evaluate your product • test your product	• evaluate the finished product • analyse the sales figures • establish future plans for the business Fig. 6.53

Improving efficiency in a business

Just as you evaluate your Design & Technology product to see whether it can be improved, and analyse the way you produced it, businesses evaluate their products. One of the main reasons why business and industry keeps changing is because of design. If you look around you, you can see that buildings, furniture, computers, cars and clothes all have to be designed, planned and made to work.

In D&T, you will learn to:
estimate the time taken, and the resources required, to complete each task and take this into account in your planning
reflect on how you went about a task, and how you might plan your next task differently
allocate tasks when leading a team
work together to establish criteria for appraisal of design and technological activity

A good designer has to balance three factors when designing a product:

1 the product must work properly;

2 the product should be pleasing to the eye, and satisfy the consumer;

3 the product must suit the market.

If the design and production methods for goods and services are not carefully analysed and evaluated, then businesses begin to fail. Designers in Research and Development Departments look at the results of market research, and the sampling of prototypes, before modifying their designs. Goods and services are often redesigned and presented as new products. Production Managers seek to improve their production methods in order to improve efficiency, and reduce the business's costs.

Improving efficiency in Design & Technology

How can you improve the way that you work in your Design & Technology activities, making them more efficient? Think about each stage of a project that you have done recently, and see if you can think of ways to improve it.

QUESTIONNAIRE

Male ☐   Female ☐

What would you want to keep in a jewellery box?

Necklaces ☐

Rings ☐

Earrings ☐

Cuff-links ☐

Bracelets ☐

Bangles ☐

Other ☐ _ _ _ _ _ _ _

EVALUATION

I have compared my box with my specification and it meets all the criteria except it cost more than I planned – £6 instead of £5.

I tested my box by putting some jewellery in it. I also asked the people who completed my questionnaire what they thought of the finished box. They all agreed it was very practical and well made, though some thought it could have been more colourful.

If I were to do this project again I would set myself a larger budget and also think about painting the finished box. I am very pleased with the actual design of the box.

During this project I have learnt to use the sanding machine.

Katy Bradbury   9QU

DESIGN BRIEF

I am going to design and make a container for storing jewellery.

SPECIFICATION

Essential criteria

My container design must:

1. Be made of wood.

2. Be made in 8 weeks.

3. Be strong enough for everyday use.

4. Be large enough to contain a variety of jewellery.

5. Have a suitable lid.

Desirable criteria

My container design should:

1. Be possible for me to make by myself, in the allocated time.

2. Be attractive with a polished, varnished or

ASSEMBLY DRAWING

All parts are sanded and fixed together using screws (lid handle), PVA (base and lid) and nails (framework of box). The outside of the box is beeswaxed and then polished.

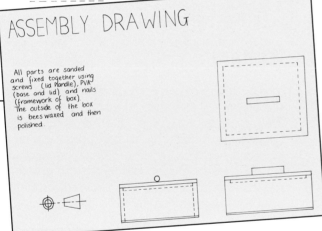

SKETCHES

Fig. 6.54 Some of the stages of a Design & Technology project

Economies of scale

Why does a pack of three Lion bars not cost three times as much as a single Lion bar? There are many advantages to producing a product on a large scale rather than on a small scale. These are called **economies of scale**:

● fixed costs for a business may remain the same, no matter how many goods are produced
● raw materials can be purchased in bulk
● large companies can take advantage of job specialisation.

However, being a big business can bring disadvantages. It is possible for a business's average costs to rise as it grows bigger. Big does not always mean better! Why do you think that this might happen? Would there be any advantages in producing your Design & Technology product in large quantities?

Fig. 6.55

Personnel

As shown on page 98, people are a resource. They provide a range of different skills and experience. When people work together combining their specialist skills, goods and services can be produced which make people's lives more comfortable and enjoyable.

In business, the **Personnel Department** is concerned with everything to do with people who work for the organisation – employment, dismissals, training, discipline, pensions, wage negotiations, etc. New employees must be given a **contract of employment** which gives details of the job, the hours of work, the rate of pay, and details of holidays, pensions and disciplinary procedures to be followed.

People are selected for jobs on the basis of their qualifications, knowledge, skills, experience, attitude, and ability. What qualifications and qualities do you think an employer might be looking for in the job advertisements shown in Fig. 6.56 and Fig. 6.57?

Fig. 6.56

Fig. 6.57

Training

Caring employers usually arrange some kind of induction programme for new employees which will help them to settle in and encourage them to feel involved. This helps them to find out about the company, and where they fit into the structure. It also covers important issues, such as safety requirements. Employers benefit from having a well-motivated workforce who work efficiently.

Ongoing training for the workforce can help:

- to increase productivity, in terms of both the quantity and quality of the goods or services
- to create flexibility amongst workers
- to improve job satisfaction and morale
- employees to gain promotion and earn more money.

Types of training

Training is an important part of any job – no one can get far without it. Look out for the following opportunities for training:

- at school, where you can obtain a good, all-round basic education
- at college or university, where 'A' level, diploma and degree courses are available
- at work, where training can be arranged by consulting your employer.

The Careers Library in your school will have more details on the kind of opportunities that are available for young people to obtain training for a job.

> *In D & T, you will learn to:*
>
> identify hazards in the working environment and to take appropriate action if dangerous situations occur
>
> recognise that people are an important resource and need to be trained, organised and motivated

Staff appraisal

The **staff appraisal** is an important part of staff development and can help someone to become more aware of their own strengths and weaknesses. It is similar to profiling and records of achievement at school. Employers may use a staff appraisal to decide whether to promote someone, and to identify their training needs.

Welfare

In addition to employing, dismissing and training staff, the Personnel Department also looks after the general welfare of its workforce – it offers facilities such as canteens, sports clubs, staff outings, and medical services, etc. The Personnel Department also keeps careful records of staff absences, any problems at work, details of qualifications and training, promotion opportunities, and so on.

Fig. 6.58 Staff facilities

Safety

The Personnel Department may also be responsible for the safety of employees. There are many hazards in the workplace, and a specialist safety officer may be appointed to ensure that the company complies with the law on health and safety. How many hazards can you spot in Fig. 6.59?

The main laws concerned with health and safety are:

Health and Safety at Work, 1974

- Employers must take all reasonable care to ensure the safety of their employees
- Employees also have a duty to cooperate with the employer to ensure the safety of all workers
- Employers with five or more staff must have a written statement of the health and safety policy

Offices, Shops and Railways Premises Act, 1963

- The temperature should be above 16°C in the workplace
- There should be adequate fresh or purified air
- There should be adequate toilet and washing facilities
- There should be suitable lighting
- There should be a minimum of 12 square metres of floor area per person

Factories Act, 1961

- There should be adequate toilet and washing facilities
- The workplace should be properly heated and ventilated
- Passageways should be free from obstruction
- The floors should have non-slippery surfaces
- There should be screens on certain machinery
- Fire escapes and fire doors should not be locked or obstructed

Fig. 6.59 Hazards in the workplace

Equal opportunities

Women and men must be treated equally at work. The Equal Pay Act, 1970 (and subsequent amendments) aimed to give equal pay for women and men doing the same work. Employers should keep a woman's job open for her if she leaves temporarily to have a baby.

It is also against the law for employers to treat people differently because of their race, colour, nationality, or if they have a disability which does not affect their ability to do the job. Job sharers – where two employees agree to share a job – are entitled to the same rights as full-time employees.

Industrial relations

What can you do if you are not happy at work? In a small organisation, you may approach your boss directly, but a large organisation usually has a more formal system of communication. Workers in the same industry sometimes join together to form **trade unions** who will negotiate with the company on the workers' behalf. Employers need to run their business as efficiently as possible, which means trying to keep their costs down. Trade unions try to obtain the best possible wages and conditions for workers. Successful industrial relations is about both sides coming together to discuss and negotiate their needs and problems.

EXTRAS

1. Ask a friend or relative if you can look at their contract of employment. What training opportunities are available to them at work?

2. Investigate the development of trade unions and professional associations, such as CBI and ACAS.

3. Employees are using the photocopier for their own private purposes. As Shop Steward, you have been asked to resolve this problem. In a group, discuss the possible solutions, and then role play this situation.

Constraints on Business

Businesses have a number of **constraints** on their activities (see Fig. 6.50). In addition to the pressure to sell their products in competition with other businesses, they must update their products because of technological developments. Businesses also have to respond to the government and pressure groups who expect them to produce goods to certain standards.

Fig. 6.60 There are many constraints on businesses

Health and safety regulations

changing consumer tastes

new technological developments

CONSTRAINTS

government legislation

pressure groups

need to make a profit

Health and Safety

Employers must take all reasonable care to ensure the safety of their employees (see page 121 for more details). It is a criminal offence for a company to allow its employees to be at risk. Employers with five or more staff must have a written statement of the company's health and safety policy. In particular, this means that they must look carefully at their methods of production. A safety representative is usually appointed to make sure that the Health and Safety at Work Act is being followed, and to 'investigate potential hazards and dangerous occurences at the workplace'.

How safe is your school? You could conduct research to find out. Look at the building itself, especially stairways. You should also consider things such as temperature, waste disposal, lighting, electrical fittings and fire regulations. Find out who the staff health and safety representative is, and what their duties are.

Consumer protection

As consumers, people have legal rights as set out in the Sale of Goods Act, 1979.

Goods must be:
● of merchantable quality (ie they must not be broken or damaged)
● as described (ie they should be as described on the content label)
● fit for a particular purpose (ie they should fulfil the task they are designed for)

Which section of the Sale of Goods Act would each of these goods not meet:
● a polyester blouse marked 'pure silk'
● a potato knife which will not even cut paper
● a kettle which keeps breaking down?

In addition, there is a voluntary organisation called the **Consumers' Association** which tests ranges of goods and services. Their findings, including advice on the 'best buys' are published in *Which?* magazine.

The **British Standards Institution** (BSI) sets standards for goods and services and awards its 'kitemark' to those which meet its standards.

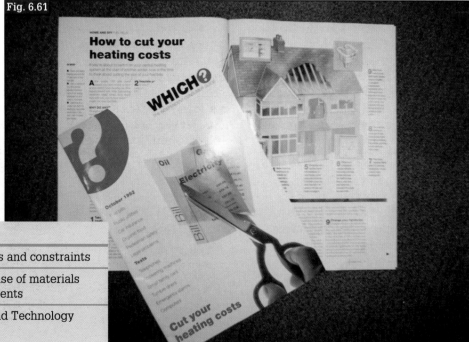

Fig. 6.61

In D&T, you will learn to:
set objectives and identify resources and constraints
be aware of the dangers of the misuse of materials and equipment and the risk of accidents
investigate the effects of Design and Technology activity on the environment

Pressure groups

Organisations such as the Consumers' Association, Friends of the Earth and Greenpeace hope to influence the decisions of business and industry. These are called **pressure groups**. Recently, environmental pressure groups have influenced companies to change their policies on the use of CFCs (chlorofluorocarbons) in aerosols. Animal rights groups openly attack organisations who use animals for testing food, chemicals and drugs. There have been attempts to free animals and destroy premises, which have resulted in companies spending money on increased security, thereby increasing operating costs.

Fig. 6.62 Technological advances can damage the environment

The environment

Large-scale disasters, such as the chemical leak at Chernobyl, make people aware that technological developments can endanger lives. More and more people are becoming aware of the damage to the environment from modern industry on both a large scale and a small scale. In addition to well-known, organised pressure groups, there are smaller, more local groups of people who want to put pressure on businesses to change their operations. The things they are concerned about include water, air and noise pollution, the danger resulting from traffic congestion, the danger of derelict areas, and waste disposal (particularly toxic waste such as chemical and nuclear waste).

Can you think of other concerns? Technological developments may benefit some sections of the community but, at the same time, they damage others. Pressure groups are usually concerned with reducing the social costs of technological developments.

Government

The government also has some control and influence over businesses. In addition to the laws that are passed to protect the consumer, the employee and the environment, there are other constraints imposed on businesses. These include taxation, national insurance, credit restrictions, export restrictions, land use, public expenditure, etc. What can you find out about these constraints?

The government makes the 'rules'. When the rules change, some people lose out and others benefit. In the early 1990s there were a number of 'charters' published – the Citizens' Charter, Parents' Charter, Patients' Charter, etc which set out the rights of individuals. How have these charters affected business organisations?

The European dimension

As countries in the European Community work closer together to develop trading policies, decisions made in Brussels can affect businesses in the United Kingdom. For example, Common Market decisions about acceptable levels of meat in sausages, or ingredients in chocolate, could threaten some of the food which is part of everyday life.

Fig. 6.63

EXTRAS

1. In a group, discuss what the costs and benefits would be if the government passed a new law to make Sunday trading legal?

2. If a nuclear power station was sited in your area, what would be the costs and benefits for the local inhabitants, and the country as a whole? Discuss this in a group.

7 ENERGY

It is energy that makes a bulb light up, a car move, a ball bounce and a baby cry. Energy is used whenever work is done – whenever there is heat, light, sound or movement. Machines use energy, plants use energy and people use energy. If you work hard you will become hungry and tired. This happens because you are using up your energy store. You can replace your energy by eating. Activities such as cycling, disco dancing and playing football are called 'energetic' because they use up a lot of energy.

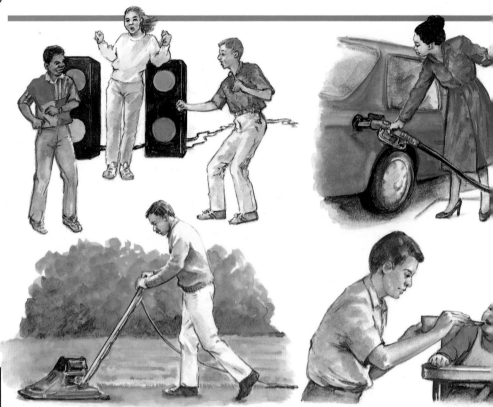

Above: Fig. 7.2 Oil from under the sea

Right: Fig. 7.3 The Aswan dam on the River Nile in Egypt

	In D & T , you will learn to:
	know that using energy affects comfort and convenience
	recognise that a source of energy is required to make things work
	know that energy can be a significant cost in manufacture and in the use of a product or system

Where does energy come from?

The energy you use comes from the food you eat. You can read more about this source of energy in chapter 5. The energy that is used to make a car move or an aeroplane fly comes from the fuel that is put in it. Fuel, like food, contains energy but how did it get there?

The ultimate source of energy is the sun. Much of the sun's energy that we use has been stored for millions of years within the Earth in the form of fossil fuels such as coal, gas and oil. These are known as **non-renewable** (or capital) energy sources because they are stored reserves of energy that cannot be replaced once they have been used. There are other sources of energy known as **renewable** (or income) energy sources. These are energy sources that can be replaced, such as energy from water power, wind power and the sun.

In the past, water power has been used as an energy source by watermills. Nowadays, hydro-electric power stations, like the Aswan dam, use water power to generate electrical energy which can then be used to do work.

Energy for comfort and convenience

Heat is a frequently used form of energy but it would be very inconvenient to have to use a coal fire to boil a kettle or to dry your hair. It is far more convenient to use electricity as an energy source for work of this type.

The electricity that is used to make life easier and more convenient has had to be converted from some other energy source. Power stations provide people's homes, schools and industries with this vital and convenient energy source. The power station gets its energy from coal, oil or nuclear fuels and then converts it into electricity. However, it is not really electrical energy that is boiling the water in your kettle – it is **heat energy**. The element in an electric kettle converts the electrical energy into heat energy. Energy is continually being converted from one form to another. This is known as an **energy chain**.

Right: Fig. 7.4 Energy conversion
Below: Fig 7.5 An energy chain

A car engine converts the energy stored in petrol into movement energy

A loudspeaker converts electrical energy into sound energy

An electric motor converts electrical energy into movement energy

A torch converts the electrical energy stored in its batteries into light energy

Electrical energy

Fossil fuel

Heat energy

Energy costs money

While it is very pleasant to have a warm house during the winter, it is important to recognise that the energy used must be paid for. The cost of energy used in the home can be high but the cost of energy used in manufacturing industry is many times greater.

Manufacturing processes that use a lot of heat, such as steel making, use so much energy that train loads of coal are needed to keep the processes operating. The cost of the energy used is a major contribution to the cost of the raw material for ships, lorries, cars and even knives

and forks. There are also energy costs for importing raw materials into the country and for delivering goods to the shops.

Energy Under Control

Design & Technology is often concerned with making effective use of energy. This means controlling energy in order to bring about the results that you intend. There are three main forms of energy that you are likely to use and need to control – **mechanical energy**, **electrical energy** and **heat energy**.

Mechanical energy

Every moving object has mechanical energy. The object needs energy to get it going and then, once it is moving, it has energy of its own. When you throw a ball, you put some of your stored energy into throwing the ball to launch it into the air. Your stored energy is not lost – it is converted into movement energy. This is also known as kinetic energy.

Stored energy is known as potential energy because it has the potential to do work. Springs, elastic bands and balloons are devices that can store mechanical energy. Clocks and clockwork toys have large springs in them. When you wind them up the energy is stored by the spring. This energy can be released very slowly by using a mechanical system. The springs of some clocks take 400 days to unwind and release all their stored energy. Sometimes springs release their stored energy very quickly, like a pin ball machine. It takes longer to pull back the pin than it does for the spring to fire the ball. In your Design & Technology activities there will be many occasions when you can make use of stored mechanical energy.

Fig. 7.6 Movement energy

Fig. 7.7 Stored energy

In D&T, you will learn to:
use a variety of energy devices
take into account the characteristics of different energy sources when designing products
take account of the effects of transferring and using energy in your designing and making
use methods of releasing and transferring energy in systems

Electrical energy

The control of electrical energy is something that you do all the time. When you switch on a light, a radio or a television you are controlling electrical energy. Electricity is the primary source of energy for most things in the home. This has not always been the case, and many places in the world still do not have electricity. Electricity is such a convenient, easily controlled source of energy that it is hard to imagine life without it.

In your Design & Technology activities in school you can use electrical energy for many of the things that you make. You will probably find that a battery is the most convenient and safest supply of electrical energy. You can easily convert the electrical energy stored in a battery into movement, light and sound energy.

Some devices use very little energy and the energy stored in the battery lasts a long time. The tiny batteries used in digital watches sometimes last for years. The same battery used to power a watch with hands does not last as long. This is because micro-electronic devices, such as digital watches, have no moving parts and require very little energy. Small PP3 batteries will last a long time in most electronic devices that you make but they will not last very long if they are required to provide the energy source for motors and mechanical devices.

It is a good idea to include an indicator light in a product to show when it is turned on. This will remind you to switch off and save energy from being drained from the battery. However, don't forget that the indicator light will also be using energy.

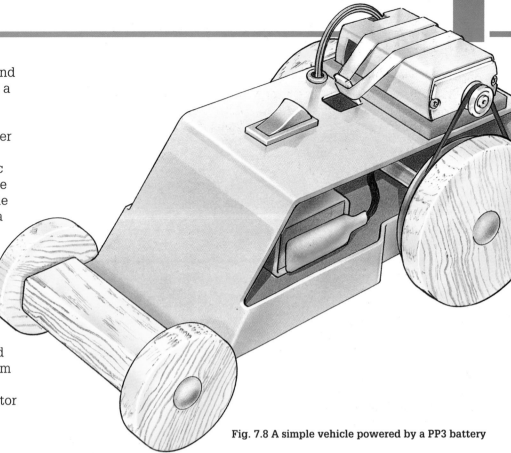

Fig. 7.8 A simple vehicle powered by a PP3 battery

Fig. 7.9

Fig. 7.10

Heat energy

Heat energy can be used to bring about useful changes in some materials. When a hard plastic material, like acrylic, is heated it becomes soft and easy to work with. Heat is also used for firing clay so that it becomes hard (see Fig. 7.9).

Cooking food is one of the most common ways of controlling heat energy. When food is being cooked it needs a controlled input of heat energy for a precise length of time. If you cook food at the wrong temperature, or for too long, it will be ruined. Fig. 7.10 shows a cake that has been cooked at the right temperature, and for the right length of time.

EXTRAS

1. Find out how an oven controls the heat energy used for cooking so that the food does not get burned.

2. Find out how a low-energy indicator light can be easily connected to a battery supply to show that it has been left on (see page 135).

Energy Conservation

Conservation of energy is a very important issue. Fig. 7.11 shows when the non-renewable energy reserves are expected to run out if they continue to be used at the current rate. One way of making them last longer is to conserve (save) them.

Recycling

All manufacturing processes use energy. However, if the products manufactured can be recycled and reused then energy will be saved. Bottle banks and other recycling schemes allow people to play their part in conserving energy.

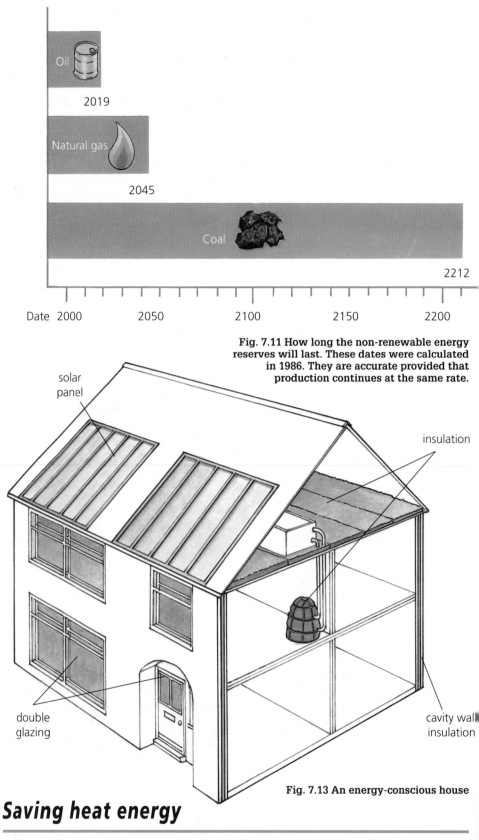

Fig. 7.11 How long the non-renewable energy reserves will last. These dates were calculated in 1986. They are accurate provided that production continues at the same rate.

Oil 2019
Natural gas 2045
Coal 2212

Date 2000   2050   2100   2150   2200

Fig. 7.12 Saving both resources and energy

	In D & T, you will learn to:
	investigate the effects of design and technological activity on the environment, and take account of its impact
	recognise potential conflicts between the needs of individuals and of society
	recognise that a solution may result in problems in other areas
	know that costs include time, people, skills, equipment and materials

Fig. 7.13 An energy-conscious house

solar panel

insulation

double glazing

cavity wall insulation

Saving heat energy

At home and at school the main form of energy that is wasted is heat energy. It is lost through the roof, walls, windows, doors and even the floor. Insulation, draught-proofing and double glazing will reduce the energy loss and reduce the fuel bills at the same time. Heat energy is also lost through carelessness – leaving doors and windows open, leaving the heating on when nobody is in the house and having the heating turned up too high.

Alternative energy

Another way to make the world's energy reserves last longer is to encourage the use of alternative energy sources. This means using renewable energy sources instead of the more common non-renewable energy reserves whenever possible.

Many houses have solar panels installed on their roofs. These use the sun's energy to heat water for domestic use in the house. Solar cells convert sunlight directly into electricity. They also provide the power source for satellites and spacecraft (see Fig. 7.14).

A power station at Rance on the coast of northern France generates electricity from the rise and fall of the tide (see Fig. 7.15). Wind energy can also be used to generate electricity (see Fig. 7.16). Even though it takes 2000 windmills to produce the same energy output as one conventional power station and, of course, the wind needs to be blowing, this alternative energy source will become more attractive as fossil fuels begin to run out.

Fig. 7.14

Fig. 7.16

Fig. 7.15

Nuclear energy

The fuel for nuclear energy is uranium. It is a non-renewable energy source but it is so concentrated that 1 kg of uranium can produce as much energy as 100 000 kg of coal. This means that the Earth's reserves of uranium will last a very long time. Unfortunately, nuclear fission, the process used to release the energy, produces harmful radioactive waste which remains harmful for hundreds of years.

Many people are very concerned about the danger of contamination that can result from the transportation and storage of nuclear waste.

There is also much concern about the risk of accidents at nuclear power stations. In 1986, a nuclear reactor exploded at Chernobyl in Ukraine, resulting in the deaths of many people and vast areas of land becoming contaminated.

Technology often involves making difficult decisions. Fossil fuels will not last for ever – there will come a time when there will be no coal, oil or gas left. Increasing the use of nuclear energy will conserve fossil fuels but the risks involved will remain.

EXTRAS

1. Examine the packaging of some of the things that you buy. Could it be reused or redesigned to reduce the waste? Try to estimate what additional costs have been added to the price of the product because of the packaging – for example, the salaries of the designers.

2. In a group discuss the implications of the increased use of nuclear power. Where do you think the waste should be stored or dumped?

8 SYSTEMS

A system is a collection of artefacts or elements, which work together to perform a task. The elements in a system can be people – in a school or a business, for example, or they can be a set of rules that people have to follow, such as a one-way system for traffic control. You, too, are a system – a biological system. You are made of lots of smaller sub-systems – a blood system, a respiratory system, a movement system, and a control system. However, this chapter only concerns systems involving artefacts. These systems can be **electronic**, **mechanical** or **structural**. A bicycle consists of all three types of system. The lights form an electronic system, the gears form a mechanical system and the frame forms a structural system.

A system has three parts – the **input**, the **process** and the **output**. A system can best be shown as a diagram, using boxes for the input, the process and the output. These boxes contain a few words of explanation. Fig. 8.1 shows a diagram for the electrical system of a personal stereo in action. Fig. 8.2 shows a diagram for the mechanical system of a door lock. Fig. 8.3 shows a diagram for the structural system of a book shelf.

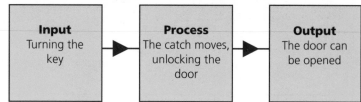

| **Input** Turning the key | **Process** The catch moves, unlocking the door | **Output** The door can be opened |

Fig. 8.2 A mechanical system

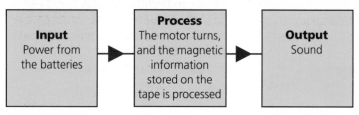

| **Input** Power from the batteries | **Process** The motor turns, and the magnetic information stored on the tape is processed | **Output** Sound |

Fig. 8.1 An electronic system

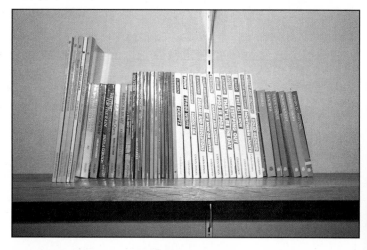

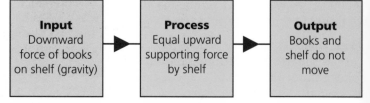

| **Input** Downward force of books on shelf (gravity) | **Process** Equal upward supporting force by shelf | **Output** Books and shelf do not move |

Fig 8.3 A structural system

In D&T, you will learn to:

know that systems have inputs, processes and outputs and recognise these in a variety of simple systems

recognise that the control of a system involves inputs, outputs, feedback and stability of that system

Control

Most things that you do require some kind of continuous **control**. When you ride a bicycle, for example, you use the handlebars, pedals and brakes to keep yourself balanced and going where you want to go. Systems are usually controlled by people, or by electronics. For example, a simple heating system for a room could consist of an open fire. When you are cold you light the fire, and when you are warm enough you put it out. You control whether or not the fire is lit. Because *you* control the lighting of the fire, you become part of the system.

Fig. 8.4 A simple heating system

Feedback loops

A more complex heating system for a house is central heating. A boiler heats the water, which is then pumped around the house in pipes to radiators which heat the rooms. This system can be manually controlled – you turn the boiler on and off – or it can be automatically controlled by electronics, using a thermostat. This device monitors the room temperature. When the room is hot enough, the thermostat switches off the heating process. When the room gets too cool, it switches the heating process on again. This way of controlling a system by checking the output is called a **feedback loop**. The information is fed back into the system to control the process – in this case, heating the house (see Fig. 8.5).

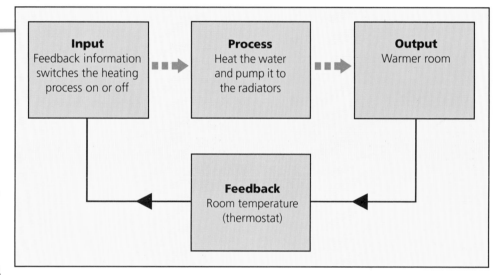

Fig. 8.5 A simple central heating control system

Another example of control is controlling an economic system. Imagine that you want some money to spend on compact discs or tapes. You decide to work to earn the money but you are not very keen on working for too long. Therefore, you need a feedback loop in the system to tell you when you have enough money, so that you can stop working. It should also tell you when you need to start working again because you are short of money (see Fig. 8.6).

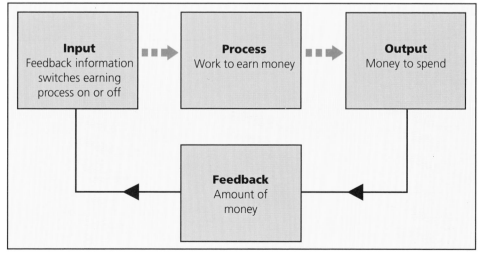

Fig. 8.6 An economic system

131

Electronic Systems

Can you imagine a world without electricity? Many of the things that you are familiar with would not work. Look at the appliances in your home. First, look in the kitchen – the refrigerator, the washing machine, the microwave, the radio, and the kettle are obvious users of electricity. These appliances are *powered* by electricity, and they are *controlled* by miniature **electronic systems**, which use very small currents of electricity. Central heating systems are controlled by electronics, even if they are gas- or oil-fired. A gas cooker may have control and lighting systems which are electronic. Without electricity, you would have to use gas lights, candles or open fires for light and heat. But it's not just in the home that we rely on electricity and electronics. The technological world is powered by electricity, and controlled by electronics. Hospitals, schools, video-games arcades, and all communication systems need electrical power. Life would be very different in a world without electricity.

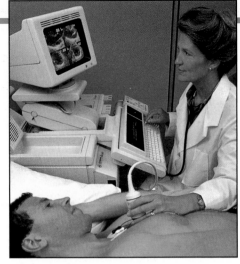

Fig. 8.7 Electronic devices in a hospital

Developments

The development of electrical devices over the last 100 years has been dramatic. Miniature electronic circuits have been made which enable a whole range of very tiny control systems to be made. In the medical world, for instance, an electronic heart-regulating controller, called a pacemaker, keeps many people alive; hearing aids can now fit right into the ear; and lasers can be used in micro-surgery. These were not available just a few years ago.

Compare the size of computers in 1960 with those in the 1990s. In 1960, powerful computers required large air-conditioned rooms, and were usually only found in universities. In the 1990s, a computer of similar power can fit into a pocket organiser (see Fig. 8.9). Computers in 1960 cost many thousands of pounds, but they cost less than fifty pounds in the 1990s.

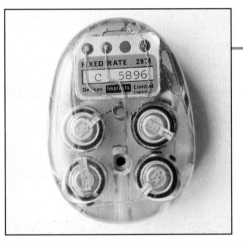

Fig. 8.8 A pacemaker

All this miniaturisation has been made possible by the invention of **integrated circuits**. These small devices can contain from a few to many thousands of separate electronic switches. These are etched on to a chip of silicon which is only a few millimetres square. A direct result of the introduction of electronic control has been a change in the work pattern for many people in industry and commerce. The use of electronically controlled robots on assembly lines means that many repetitive tasks that people used to do manually, all day long, are now done by robots. The use of computers, word processors, fax machines and calculators has greatly affected work in thousands of offices.

Fig. 8.9

In D & T, you will learn to:

recognise that a source of energy is required to make things work

take into account the characteristics of different energy sources when designing products

Power Sources

Every system needs a power source to enable it to work. A door handle needs pressure from your hand, a remote controller for a model car needs both hand pressure and electrical energy. Weather systems need energy from the sun in order to operate. You need food energy to enable you to live.

Fig. 8.10 Mains power

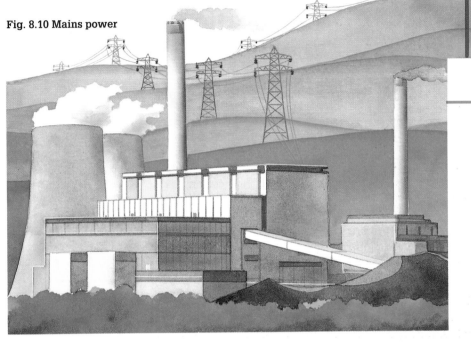

Electrical energy

Electrical energy for most electrical appliances in the home, such as the cooker and television, comes from the mains electricity supply. This energy is supplied by power stations, and sent to your home along copper or aluminium wires which are either strung between pylons or run underground. The mains electricity supply is very powerful. This power is needed to operate large appliances. It is, however, very dangerous for you to use this supply when you experiment in your project work. It can kill you if you touch the wires.

Batteries

Small amounts of electrical power can be generated by chemicals in small containers. These are called **batteries**. The chemical inside most batteries can only provide 1.5 **volts** of electricity. A volt is a measure of the pressure of the electrical energy.

Batteries are usually used in a group rather than singly. **Battery holders** (like battery compartments) have connections so that the batteries are linked together. If four 1.5 volt batteries are held together in a group of four, they can produce 6 volts (4×1.5 volts) between them. The first personal stereos that were made used four 1.5 volt batteries to drive 6 volt motors that turned the tapes. Newer styles of personal stereos use 3 volt motors, so only two 1.5 volt batteries are needed. Some batteries are grouped by the manufacturer and sold as a complete package. They look like single batteries, but under the casing there are two, four or six batteries connected to each other. A 9-volt PP3

Fig. 8.11

battery, for instance, contains six small batteries grouped together. A 9-volt PP9 battery also contains six batteries but it is bigger, heavier and more expensive. It will, however, last much longer than a PP3 battery, because it contains more chemicals.

The different sizes of batteries are designed for different purposes. Look to see how many batteries there are in your cycle lamps, what voltage they are, and what voltage bulbs are used. Cycle lamps use much bigger batteries than personal stereos. Small light-weight batteries are used for a personal stereo, but size and weight are not the most important considerations for lamps. They need batteries that will last for a long time.

Simple Electrical Systems

Fig. 8.12 shows an electrical system. The battery, the switch and the bulb are joined by wires to form a complete loop – a **circuit**. A circuit is like a running track – it forms a complete linked track to allow the electricity to flow around it. If the track is broken, or incomplete, the electricity cannot even start to flow. A mechanical device, called a switch, allows the circuit to be complete or broken when required. There are many different types of switches. An electronic component catalogue gives nearly as many choices of switches as a mail order catalogue gives choices of clothes.

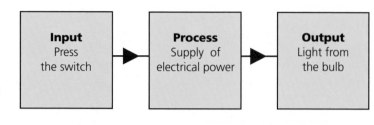

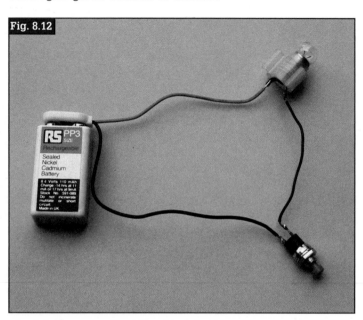

Fig. 8.12

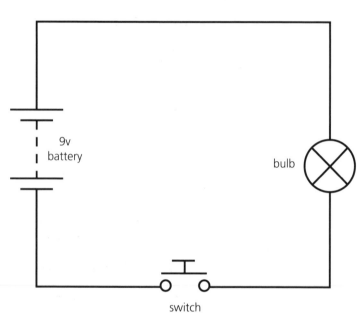

Making the connections

The components in an electrical circuit are connected by the thin copper wires covered in a plastic material. Copper is a good **conductor** of electricity, allowing it to flow easily. Plastic is a very bad conductor of electricity. In fact it is an **insulator**, which means that it allows no electrical current to flow. When you connect wires together, the insulating cover must first be removed, and then the copper wires can be joined. The insulating cover is very important – it allows you to pick up cables and wires without the electricity passing into you and giving you an electric shock. It also prevents the copper wires from touching each other in the wrong place, causing a 'short circuit'. This may result in a simple failure of the bulb to work but, on more complex systems, it could lead to a system failure with drastic and expensive results.

Fig. 8.13 Electrical components

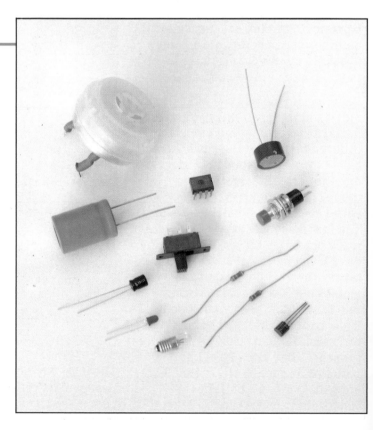

> *In D & T, you will learn to*
>
> use methods of releasing and transferring energy in systems

Electric Motors

Fig. 8.14 A vehicle powered by an electric motor

Electrical systems can be used to make things move. An electric motor is a mechanical device that uses electrical energy to make a drive shaft turn. Motors can be small, such as the motors in cameras, or they can be very large industrial devices that drive large machines, such as printing presses.

The direction of the drive shaft's rotation depends on which way the electricity flows through the motor. The direction can be changed by altering the circuit, so that the electricity flows the other way through the motor. This is called changing the **polarity**. Two switches joined together, and operated by one lever, are needed for this. They are called **double-pole double-throw** switches (DPDT). The two switches, looking like gates joined together, connect the battery to the motor (see Figs. 8.15 and 8.16).

Fig. 8.16 A circuit diagram of a motor with double-pole double-throw switches

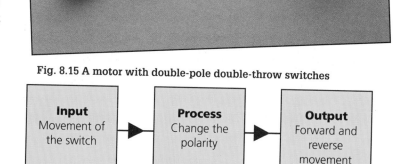

Fig. 8.15 A motor with double-pole double-throw switches

Input Movement of the switch	**Process** Change the polarity	**Output** Forward and reverse movement

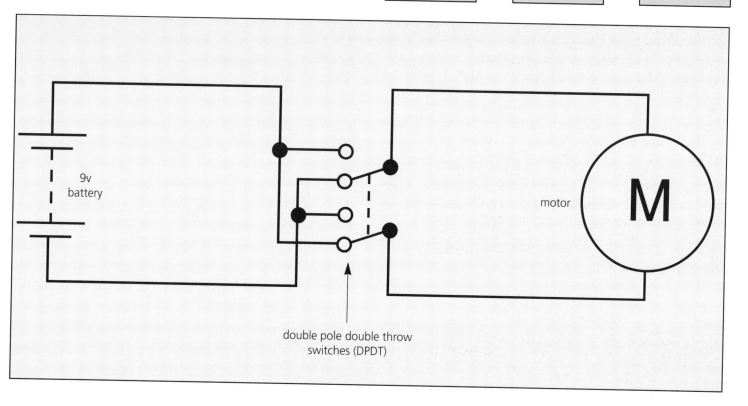

double pole double throw switches (DPDT)

Controlling Electrical Energy

Electricity flows along a wire in a manner similar to water flowing along a pipe. With water, the larger the pipe, the easier it is for water to flow. With electricity, it is the *material* the wire is made of which determines the flow (the **current**). Some materials have more **resistance** to the current than others. It's a bit like when you walk.

You normally just walk through air. You know that it is harder to walk through water. Think how hard it would be to walk through jelly! That amount of resistance would really slow you down. A brick wall would stop you altogether. With electricity, you have already seen that some materials – insulators – resist the flow of electricity altogether.

Resistors

It is possible to control the speed of a motor or the brightness of a lamp by using a component called a **variable resistor**. Just as a tap in a water system makes the flow of water increase or decrease depending on which way the tap is turned, a variable resistor controls the flow of electricity by means of a twist control. An example of this is a volume control on a radio, which controls the sound level. There are also **fixed resistors** which restrict the flow of electricity by a particular amount. This resistance is measured in **ohms**.

Fig. 8.17

Light bulbs

The wire filament in a bulb is made from a material called tungsten. It resists the flow of electricity, which makes the wire hot. As the wire is very thin, the heat produced makes the filament glow white hot. It is this white hot wire that gives off the light. The heat can also make the outside of a bulb become quite hot. Unlike motors, it doesn't matter which way the current flows through a bulb.

LEDs

Small indicator lights are found on many different electrical devices, usually to show that the device is switched on. These are not the same bulbs as light bulbs. The light given off is of a very low level – it is bright enough to be seen clearly, but it does not have to illuminate anything. These small red, green or orange lights are called **light-emitting diodes** (LEDs). Compared with ordinary bulbs they use very little electricity, and they last a long time.

LEDs are delicate devices that differ from bulbs in a number of ways:

- They do not have a wire filament but a small piece of silicon that produces the light.

- They give off very little light or heat.

- They do not light if they are connected the wrong way round in a circuit.

- They only need a small current of electricity.

- They must always be used with a fixed resistor to stop excess current from damaging them.

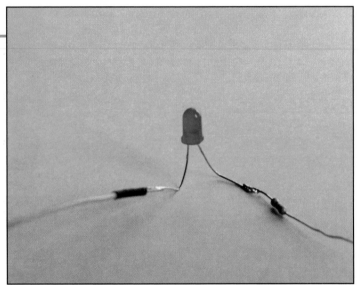
Fig. 8.18 An LED and resistor

Using a number of LEDs, it is possible to make letters and words. This is a method used to make lettering on display boards when simple words are needed. Motorway warning signs use this method, but using larger and brighter lights.

Buzzers

Some warning systems do not use lights, they use sound, for example, a fire alarm. In the classroom, buzzers can easily be used in a warning system. They are usually powered by a 6 volt or a 9 volt battery. You must make sure you use the right battery for the buzzer.

In D&T, you will learn to:		
recognise that materials have different working properties		
use a variety of energy devices		

Sensing Systems

Electronic systems are very good at sensing changes in the environment.

Sensing light

A transistor is a 'switch' that is operated by a tiny electric current rather than by the pressure of a finger. Transistors can be used as switches in many ways. When they are controlled by **light sensors**, for instance, they can 'switch on' lighting circuits when it gets dark. A light sensor includes a kind of resistor which changes its resistance depending on how much light falls on it. When the resistance is lowered, the sensor lets through the tiny current which works the transistor and switches on the circuit.

Circuits like these, including light sensors and transistors, are used to control street lights, illuminated signs, etc.

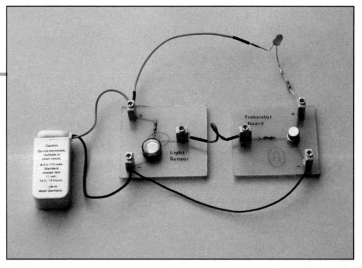
Fig. 8.19 A light-sensing system

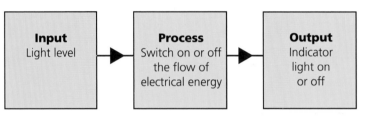

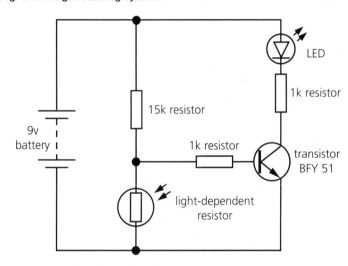

Sensing temperature

Circuits controlled by changes in temperature can be made using transistors and **thermistors**. Thermistors change their resistance according to their temperature and can be used with transistors to 'switch on' heating or cooling circuits when they are needed.

Temperature-sensing systems are used in agriculture, industry and the home. In agriculture they are used, for instance, to control the temperature of greenhouses. In industry, chemical reactions need to be controlled by temperature-sensing systems, so that they are safe. In the home, there are temperature-sensing systems in washing machines and central heating thermostats.

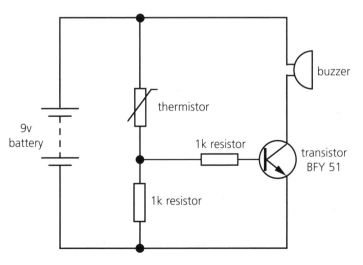
Fig. 8.20 A temperature-sensing system

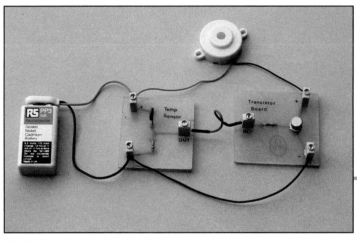

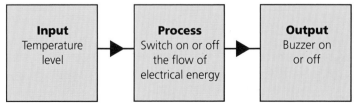

Integrated Circuits

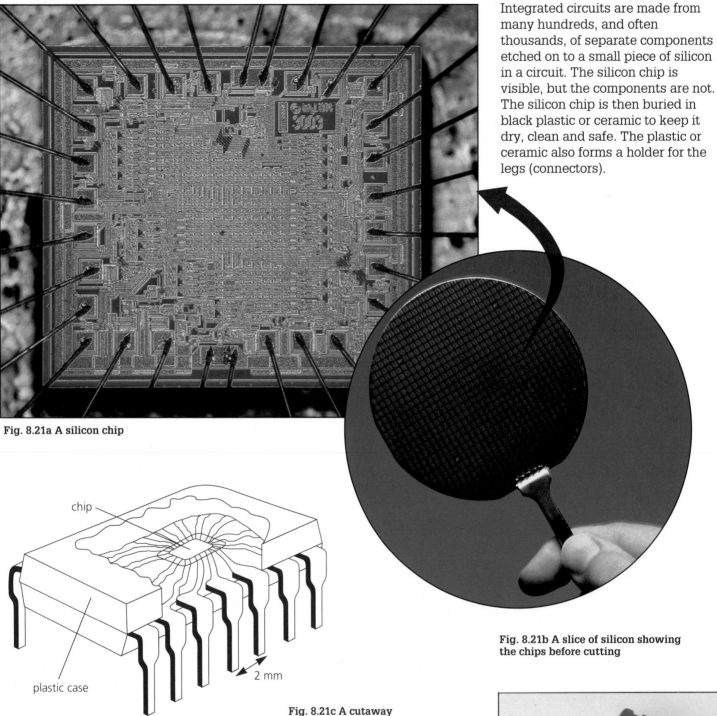

Integrated circuits are made from many hundreds, and often thousands, of separate components etched on to a small piece of silicon in a circuit. The silicon chip is visible, but the components are not. The silicon chip is then buried in black plastic or ceramic to keep it dry, clean and safe. The plastic or ceramic also forms a holder for the legs (connectors).

Fig. 8.21a A silicon chip

Fig. 8.21b A slice of silicon showing the chips before cutting

chip

plastic case

2 mm

Fig. 8.21c A cutaway view of an integrated circuit

Flashing LEDs

Flashing LEDs look very similar to standard LEDs (see page 136). However, flashing LEDs contain an integrated circuit. The circuit is designed to make the LED switch on and off continuously. The circuit also contains a built-in resistor so an extra fixed resistor is not required. When the LED is connected to a 9 volt battery, it flashes. When ordinary LEDs are connected to the flashing LED, like a string of sausages, they all flash together (and there is no need for extra resistors).

Fig. 8.22

138

Modelling Circuits

It takes a long time to build a circuit properly, using separate components and a printed circuit board (see pages 140–141). It is not good designing practice to build a complete circuit if you are not absolutely sure it will work, so you should always **model** the circuit first, to test your design. On a model it is easy to modify your ideas until the circuit works properly. It would be good to be able to design circuits that work first time, all the time, but designing is not like that. Good designing requires development and improvement, so it is necessary to model and test your ideas.

The method of modelling will depend on what equipment is available, and how complicated the circuit is. A simple method is to use a piece of wood with screws and screw cups to provide a means of gripping the wires and components (see Fig. 8.23). Components can be fastened to a board to form a unit (see Fig. 8.24). Various units can then be coupled together in a variety of different ways.

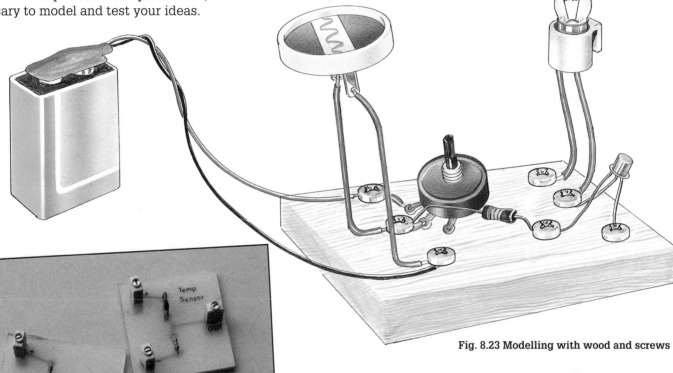

Fig. 8.23 Modelling with wood and screws

Fig. 8.24 Units built in the classroom

Complete units of sensors, control and outputs can be built (or purchased) to enable a whole range of different systems to be designed and tested easily. It is possible to buy ready-made units which can be joined together in many different ways, such as the Locktronics board shown in Fig. 8.25. This figure also shows a prototype modelling board which can also be used to model a circuit.

Fig. 8.25 A Locktronics system and prototype modelling board

139

Making a Circuit Board

To build a circuit for use in a working system, you will need to produce a circuit board and solder the components on to it. The circuit board forms the backbone of the circuit, providing support for all the other components.

Printed circuit boards (pcbs) are made from layers of different materials. The main part of the board is a glass-reinforced plastic (grp) laminate – the same sort of material that can be used to build boats. Underneath this is a copper layer that will allow the electricity to flow from one component to another. This copper must be made into tracks to form the 'wires' for the flow of the electric current. Components that are to be part of the circuit must have 'legs' to connect them to the pcb. The legs are placed in holes drilled through the pcb. The legs stick through the laminate and are soldered on to the copper tracks below.

Fig. 8.26 A printed circuit board

Drawing the pattern of copper tracks is part of the skill of designing circuits. Circuits are not only designed on paper. A circuit-drawing program can be used to design simple or more complicated circuits on a computer. The design is then printed on to paper by a plotter.

Fig. 8.27 Transferring the design to the pcb

tracing paper

pcb

Resistor

LED

Fuse

Battery Connections

+

−

Etching

Whatever way you design your circuit, you need to use an acid-resistant method to transfer your lines on to the copper layer. The rest of the copper is then dissolved away with acid, leaving the tracks of copper which will connect the components. Removing metal by dissolving it in acid is called **etching**. This can be dangerous as acid burns skin, so great care must be taken. A proper etching tank with safety gear, such as goggles and gloves, must be used. You should also hold the circuit board with tongs. All the implements and the circuit board must be washed thoroughly in water afterwards.

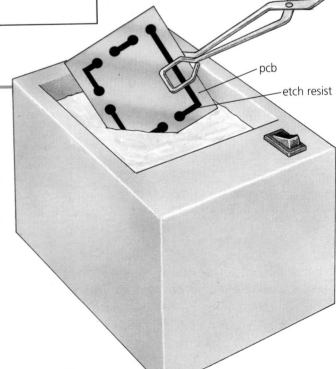

pcb

etch resist

Fig. 8.28 Etching a circuit in an etch tank

In D & T, you will learn to:
understand that it may be necessary to practice an operation to improve quality
be aware of the dangers of the misuse of materials and equipment, and the consequent risk of accidents

Drilling

The holes for the components must be drilled into the pcb. The size of the components and their pin spacing must be carefully measured because the components can be damaged if they are forced into holes which are not quite in the right place. These holes are usually made with a 1 mm drill and they must line up exactly with the connecting tracks.

hollow solder containing flux

Multi-core solder

Soldering iron stand

Fig. 8.30 Soldering tools

Fig. 8.29 Drilling the pcb

Soldering

The components and wires are joined to the circuit by **soldering**. Solder is a metal which is melted and used like glue. A soldering iron is used to heat the solder until it melts. The pieces of metal being joined together must also be heated in order for the solder to stick to them. The solder gives off a little smoke as it is melted because there is a fine core of resin in the solder wire. The resin helps the joint to work properly. Many problems in circuits often arise because of badly soldered connections. It is important, therefore, that soldering is done properly. You should practise it until you can do it well before you build a circuit.

Soldering

1 All components must be clean.

2 Place the leg or wire through the hole in the board.

3 Heat both parts of the joint with the soldering iron.

4 Apply the solder, allowing it to run into the joint.

5 Allow it to cool without moving it.

Fig. 8.31 Soldering a component on to a pcb

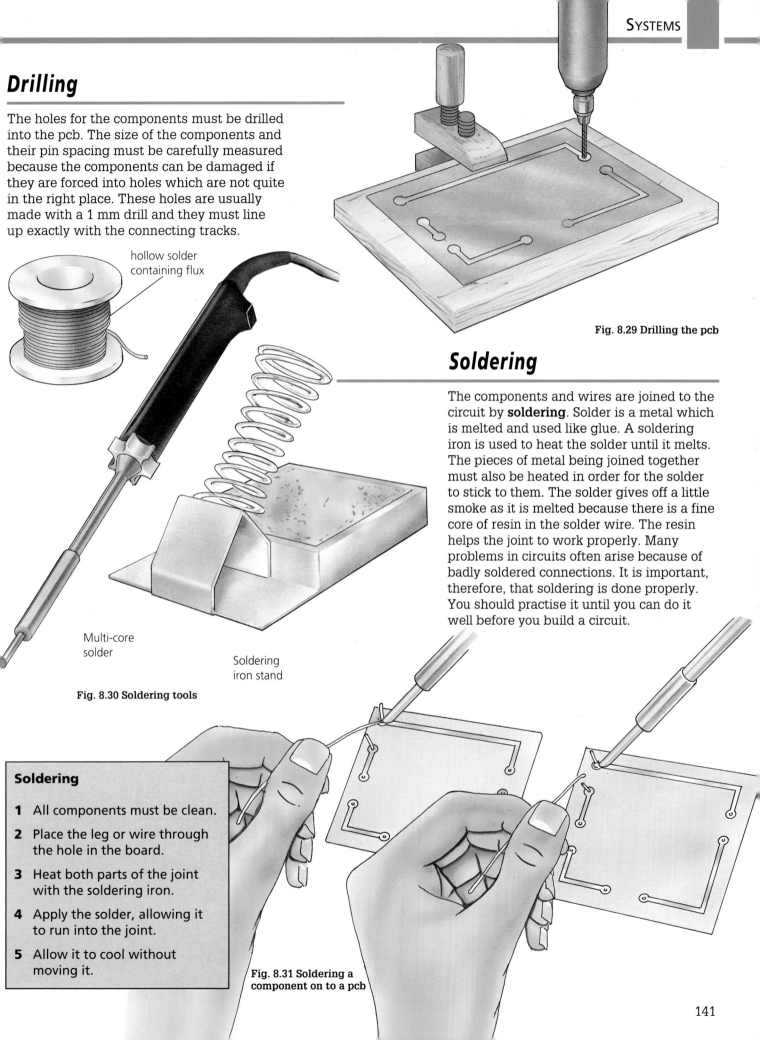

141

Mechanical Systems

A mechanism is a device with moving parts that has been designed to do a particular task. Think how many mechanisms you have used today. Water taps, light switches and door handles are all types of mechanisms, but they are so common that you probably never give them a second thought. These are examples of simple mechanisms, but there are also some very complex mechanisms, such as bicycles, sewing machines, washing machines and cars. These devices are all **mechanical systems**. They are made up of many mechanisms which work together.

Fig. 8.32

Fig. 8.33 A bicycle – a mechanical system

	In D&T, you will learn to:
	select and use mechanisms to bring about changes and control movement
	use simple mechanisms to transfer motion
	use mechanisms to change one type of motion into another
	recognise that mechanisms need to be controlled if they are to achieve their intended function

It is not very easy to look at the different mechanisms that make up a car or a washing machine, but if you examine a bicycle you can easily see the different mechanisms. If you look at Fig. 8.33 you should be able to identify the steering system, the braking system and the system that makes the bicycle move. This last system is made up of the pedals, the chain, the gears and the back wheel. It is sometimes more convenient to think of objects as complete systems rather than as individual parts that are joined together.

Design & Technology is about designing and making products. When you are designing mechanisms, it is helpful to be able to understand how the mechanisms work, and how they contribute to the system. If your bicycle does not stop, you soon realise that there may be a problem with the brakes. This is because you have an understanding of how the bicycle works, and you know that it is no good looking at the pedals or the steering to find the fault.

Mechanical systems always involve movement and energy. Like all systems they have an input, a process and an output. When riding a bicycle, the cyclist uses energy to turn the pedals – this is the input. The process is the pedals turning the chain and, through the gears, the rear wheel. The output is the work done in moving both the bicycle and the rider forwards.

The Four Types of Motion

When an object moves it is said to be in **motion**. The type of motion is described by the direction in which the object moves. Mechanical systems involve four types of motion:

Fig. 8.34a

Oscillating motion means the object swings backwards and forwards, like a grandfather clock's pendulum.

Fig. 8.34b

Linear motion means the object moves in a straight line, like a drawer.

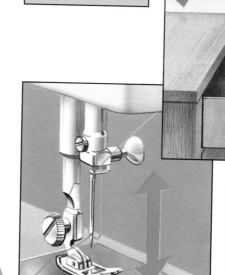

Fig. 8.34c

Rotary motion means the object goes round, like wheels and clock hands.

Reciprocating motion means the object goes backwards and forwards (or up and down) in a straight line, like a sewing machine needle.

Fig. 8.34d

One of the main functions of mechanical systems is to change motion from one type to another, that is, to change its direction. With a bicycle, for instance, the input motion is rotary, as it turns the pedals round. The output motion, however, is linear as it moves the bicycle in a straight line. A simple device, like a key in a lock, is also a mechanism for changing rotary motion to linear motion.

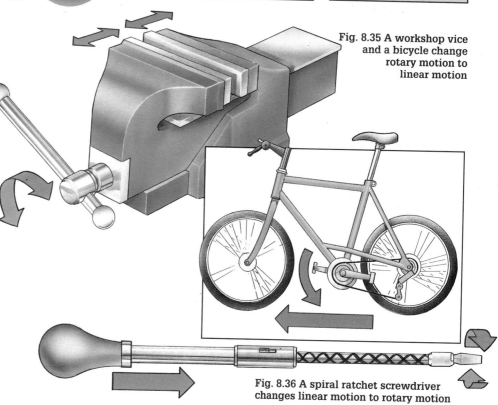

Fig. 8.35 A workshop vice and a bicycle change rotary motion to linear motion

Fig. 8.36 A spiral ratchet screwdriver changes linear motion to rotary motion

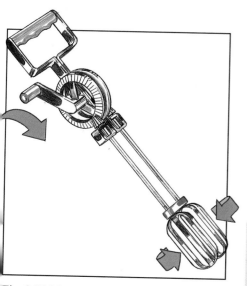

Fig. 8.37 A hand whisk transfers rotary motion in one plane into faster rotary motion in another plane

EXTRAS

1. Look around your school workshops or your kitchen at home and see how many mechanisms you can find that change and transfer motion. Make a list of them.

Mechanical Advantage

Mechanisms are designed so that people gain some advantage from using them. They enable people to do something that they could not otherwise do because it would be too hard or too slow, or just impossible. This advantage is called **mechanical advantage**.

Levers

The simplest and one of the earliest mechanisms used was the lever. It consists of a rigid bar with a fixed point on which the bar turns. This fixed point is called a **pivot**. The input is usually called the **effort** and the output is the movement of the **load** (see Fig. 8.38). The lever was probably used during the Stone Age (long before the wheel was invented) to move heavy boulders.

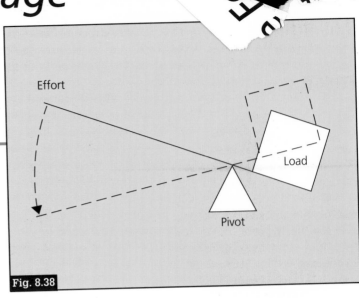

Fig. 8.38

How can such a simple mechanism gain so much mechanical advantage? The advantage is gained by not having the pivot in the middle of the lever. The effort must move the lever further than the distance that the load is moved. This means that a person has to press down a long way on the lever to move the load only a small distance. What the lever gains in its ability to lift, it loses in the distance that the handle of the lever has to move. But without the lever a heavy load could not be moved at all.

Fig. 8.39 Levers used every day

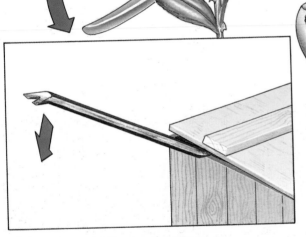

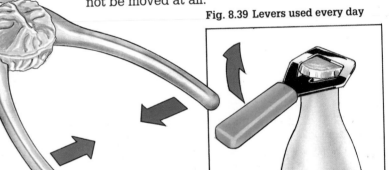

Balance and equilibrium

Balance scales and see-saws are types of levers. They work by balancing one force against another. When balance is achieved, the scales or see-saw are said to be in **equilibrium**. But equilibrium is only maintained as long as the forces balance each other.

On a see-saw two teenagers that weigh the same balance each other because the pivot is in the middle and there is no mechanical advantage. A heavy and a light teenager can balance, providing that the heavy teenager sits nearer to the pivot. If the heavy teenager is twice the weight of the light teenager then the light teenager must sit twice as far from the pivot (see Fig. 8.40).

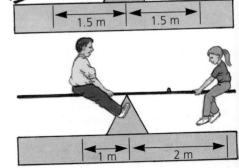

Fig. 8.40

In D&T, you will learn to:
take account of the forces which operate on and influence mechanisms when selecting a mechanism for a design

Linkages

Linkages are made by connecting levers together. They are used to link together parts of mechanical systems. They can transfer forces and bring about changes in the direction of forces.

The simple linkage in Fig. 8.41 can be used to reverse the direction of a force, for example, changing a pushing force into a pulling force. The linkage in Fig. 8.42 is used to transfer a force through 90°. This linkage is called a bell crank because it is like an old-fashioned door bell mechanism. It is also the mechanism that operates a bicycle brake (see Fig. 8.43).

The pivot point of a linkage can be positioned to gain mechanical advantage, in the same way as with a lever. If the pivot is not in the middle of the link, then one side of the link must move a further distance than the other (see Fig. 8.44). A small input force can produce a larger output force (over a shorter distance), or a small input movement can produce a larger output movement (with less force). But, as with levers, you can't have it both ways.

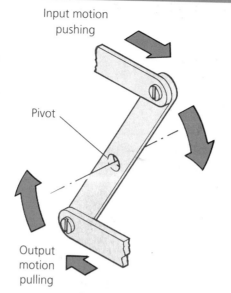

Input motion pushing

Pivot

Output motion pulling

Fig. 8.41 A simple linkage

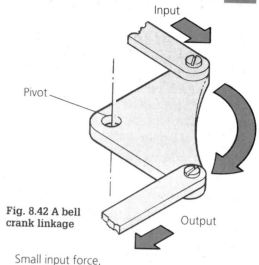

Input

Pivot

Fig. 8.42 A bell crank linkage

Output

Small input force, large input movement

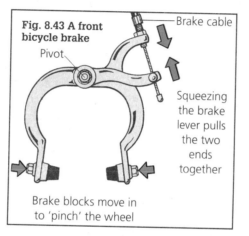

Fig. 8.43 A front bicycle brake

Brake cable

Pivot

Squeezing the brake lever pulls the two ends together

Brake blocks move in to 'pinch' the wheel

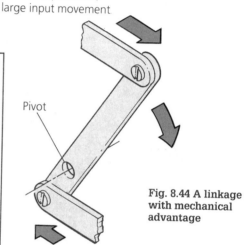

Pivot

Fig. 8.44 A linkage with mechanical advantage

Larger output force, smaller output movement

Parallel linkages

Imagine a parallelogram with corner joints that pivot. No matter how much it squashes or changes shape, the sides that are opposite each other always remain parallel (see Fig. 8.45). You may have seen this parallel link mechanism used in tool boxes with trays that open out (see Fig. 8.46). It is also used on the top of electric trains to connect the train to the overhead power lines. The joints of the parallel links on electric trains are spring-loaded so that the electrical contacts of the train are kept pressed against the overhead power lines. This mechanism is known as a **pantograph**.

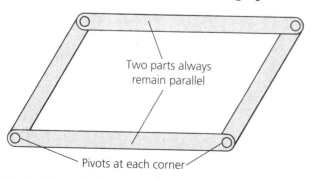

Two parts always remain parallel

Pivots at each corner

Fig. 8.45 A parallel link mechanism

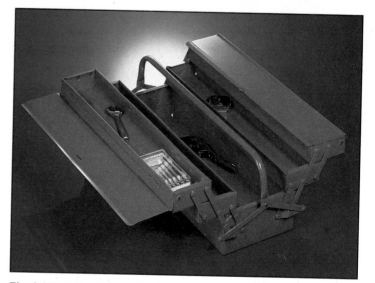

Fig. 8.46 Parallel link mechanisms used in a tool box

EXTRAS

1. Use Lego or Meccano to make a linkage mechanism, such as a bell crank or a bicycle brake.

Inclined planes

Fig. 8.47

Inclined planes are slopes and ramps. In ancient times, people used huge stones to build structures like the Pyramids and Stonehenge. The challenge for the builders was how to lift the heavy stones so that they fitted on top of other stones. The solution was to build a very long ramp (see Fig. 8.47). A mechanical advantage was gained because it is easier to push a heavy stone a long distance up a gently inclined plane than it is to lift it vertically, even a small distance. By using an inclined plane a small input force over a long distance produced a large output force over a shorter distance.

Building technology today still makes use of the inclined plane. Builders push wheelbarrows up inclined planks because it is much easier than lifting them (see Fig. 8.48).

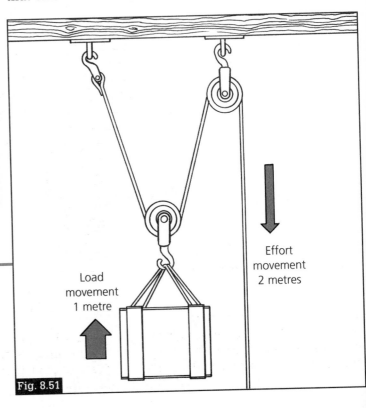

Fig. 8.48

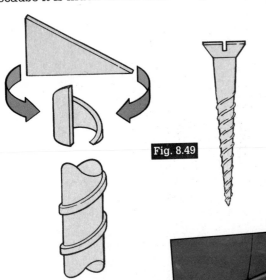

Fig. 8.49

Screw-based mechanisms usually have a large mechanical advantage. Screw jacks that are used to lift cars, and workshop vices, can be operated with little input effort to achieve a large output load.

Fig. 8.50 A screw jack being used to lift a car

Screws

Screws are inclined planes that are wrapped around a cylinder (see Fig. 8.49). You can see this if you look closely at a wood screw or a bolt. When a screw is cutting its way into wood a lot of work is being done. It is cutting through fibres, making a hole and pulling itself into the hole. It is the screw's mechanical advantage that enables it to be turned relatively easily.

Pulleys for lifting

Free-running pulley systems are often used in warehouses and factories to help lift heavy weights, such as crates and machinery. A pulley is a wheel with a groove in its rim. A two-pulley system like the one shown in Fig. 8.51 has a mechanical advantage of 2. This means that a load can be lifted using half the input effort. But the effort, of course, needs to travel twice the distance.

Load movement 1 metre

Effort movement 2 metres

Fig. 8.51

Pulleys for Changing and Transferring Motion

Pulley systems, using pulleys fixed on shafts, are used to transfer rotary motion from one place to another. They can also be used to change the speed of the motion. Pulleys must always fit tightly onto their drive shafts otherwise they will slip and effort and energy will be lost. The speed of rotation is affected by the difference in size between the **driver** pulley and the **driven** pulley. If the driver pulley is larger than the driven pulley, then the output speed will be greater than the input speed (see Fig. 8.52). If the driver pulley is smaller than the driven pulley then the output speed will be slower than the input speed (see Fig. 8.53). When pulleys of different sizes are fixed on to the same shaft (stepped pulleys) the speed can be changed by moving the belt from one pulley to another (see Fig. 8.54).

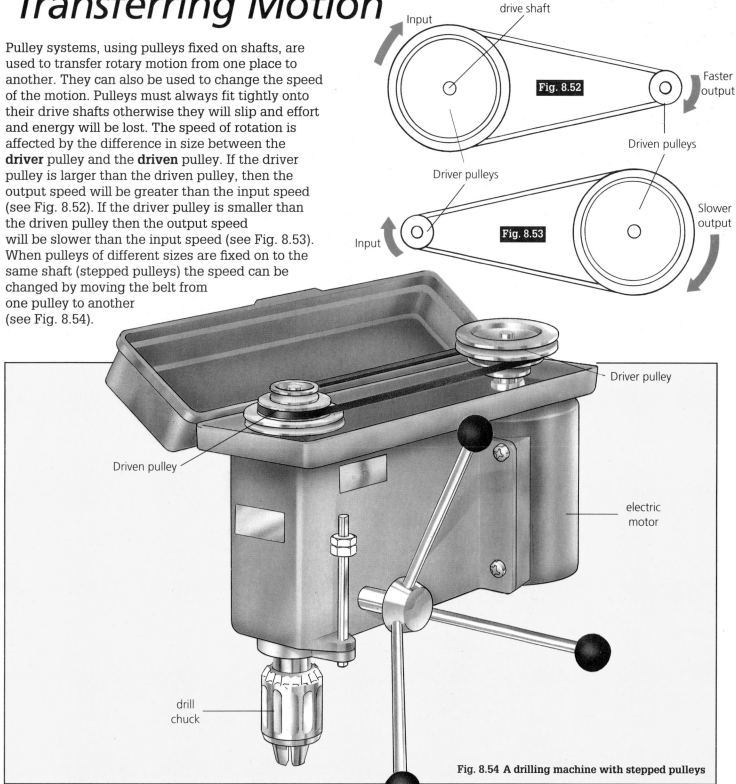

drive shaft

Input

Fig. 8.52

Faster output

Driver pulleys

Driven pulleys

Input

Fig. 8.53

Slower output

Driver pulley

Driven pulley

electric motor

drill chuck

Fig. 8.54 A drilling machine with stepped pulleys

When you are investigating mechanisms, make sure you never operate any machines with the covers open or removed.

EXTRAS

1. If a driver pulley has a diameter of 60 millimetres, what size must the driven pulley be to make it rotate twice as fast as the driver pulley? Test out your answer by making this pulley system.

147

Gears for Changing and Transferring Motion

Like pulley systems, gear systems are used to change and transfer rotary motion. Gears are wheels with teeth which are an equal distance apart. The teeth are usually on the rim of the wheel but are sometimes on the face. Most gears are made from plastic or metal, but in the past and in other cultures gears have been made from wood (see Fig. 8.55). Gear teeth are a special shape called an **involute**, and it is this shape that helps gears to run together smoothly and to transfer motion from one gear to the next. A system of gears is known as a **gear train**. Gear trains should be put together with care. They should not be too loose or too tight, otherwise energy may be wasted.

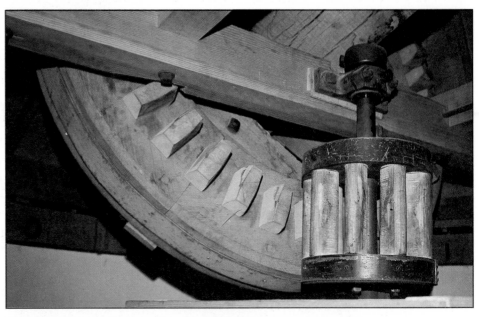

Fig. 8.55 An old wooden gear system in a windmill

Gears can be used to change speed and to change direction. The input gear to any system is called the **driver gear** and the output gear is called the **driven gear**. In a simple (or in-line) gear train, as in Fig. 8.56, the gears fitted between the driver and driven gears are called **idler gears**. They change the direction of rotation. A change in speed within a gear train is achieved by putting together gears with different numbers of teeth. If a driver gear with 40 teeth is driving a driven gear that has 20 teeth, the speed will be double. For every turn of the driver gear the driven gear will turn twice. The number of turns of one gear to another is called the **gear ratio**. The gear ratio for this gear train is 1:2 (one to two). If the driver gear has 20 teeth and the driven gear 40 teeth the gear chain will slow down. For every two turns of the driver gear the driven gear will turn once and will therefore have a gear ratio of 2:1. The number and size of idler gears between the driver and driven gear has no effect upon the gear ratio – they only change the direction.

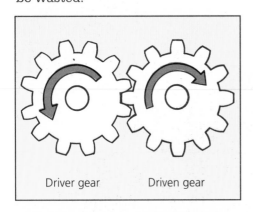

Driver gear   Driven gear

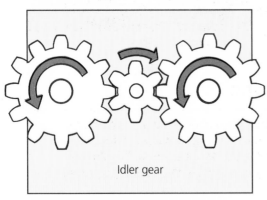

Idler gear

Fig. 8.56 Simple gear trains

In D&T, you will learn to:

identify the basic principles of how different mechanisms change speed or change motion, from one form to another

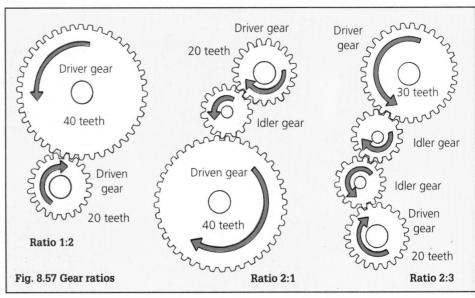

Fig. 8.57 Gear ratios

Bevel gears

Bevel gears are used in pairs to change the angle of rotation through 90° (see Fig. 8.58). Hand drills use bevel gears to both change the direction of rotation and to make the drill rotate fast.

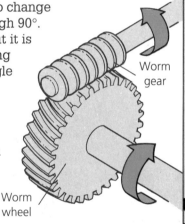

Fig. 8.58 Bevel gears

Fig. 8.59 A hand drill

Worm and wormwheel

This is another gear system to change the direction of rotation through 90°. A worm looks like a screw, but it is really a gear with only one long tooth (see Fig. 8.60). This single tooth is wrapped around a cylinder and is used to turn a gear. The gear ratio of worm drives is very low. They are often used to change the high speed of electric motors into more useful speeds.

Worm gear

Worm wheel

Fig. 8.60 Worm and wormwheel

Fig. 8.61 A small electric motor with a worm drive

Rack and pinion

Rack and pinions change motion from rotary to linear. A rack is like a flattened out gear wheel. The gear that it works with is called a pinion (see Fig. 8.62). They are used on canal lock gates and in car steering systems.

Fig. 8.62 A canal lock gate

pinion

Fig. 8.63 Rack and pinion

rack

EXTRAS

1. Using a modelling kit, make the gear trains in Fig 8.57. For what purpose do you think two idler gears would be useful?.

2. Make a gear system that has **(a)** a 1:4 ratio and **(b)** does not change direction.

149

Mechanical Efficiency

When designing a mechanical system it is important to consider its efficiency. An efficient mechanism is one that loses very little energy in doing its job. A loss of energy could mean a loss of money or a waste of resources. Cars, for example, are very inefficient mechanical systems. Only a small percentage of the potential energy of the fuel is converted by the car into movement. Most of the energy is lost in the form of friction, mechanical wear, heat, sound and exhaust fumes. Simple lever systems, like the see-saw, are very efficient. This means that most of the effort is converted to work done by the mechanism, and very little energy is lost within the system.

No matter how simple a mechanical system is, to be efficient it needs to be made with care. Its parts need to be clean and smooth, and they must fit together well and not be too loose. Often a drop of oil for lubrication will help. You may have noticed that a rusty bicycle that needs oiling is harder to pedal than one that has been well looked after.

Fig. 8.64 A car being tuned to improve its mechanical efficiency

Fig. 8.65

	In D&T, you will learn to:
	recognise how the efficiency of a mechanism can be improved when designing a product
	select and use simple mechanisms, including linkages and gearing, in making prototypes
	recognise that mechanisms can be controlled by computers
	design mechanical systems to produce a desired output from a given input

Mechanical Models and Prototypes

Making a model, to test how your design works before you make your finished product, is called **prototyping**. Making a prototype of a mechanical system before manufacturing it can save time and trouble. You cannot always be certain how a system will work until you have tried it out. Prototyping is a way of trying out a system quickly, using a modelling kit or easily workable material, such as card, coroflute, strips of wood and wire. Lego, Meccano and Fishertechnik are types of modelling kit. Gears from modelling kits can be used with wood and wire models. Hot-melt glue guns are useful for modelling with wood and junk materials, but do not use them with kits that need to be taken apart and used again.

Computer-controlled models

In manufacturing industries, computers are used to control many different machines, including robots, food mixers, drilling machines and lathes. The mechanical models in Fig. 8.66 and Fig. 8.67 were made by pupils. The movement of the crane, in Fig. 8.66, is controlled by a computer. Two electric motors position the hook, and a third electric motor raises and lowers the hook.

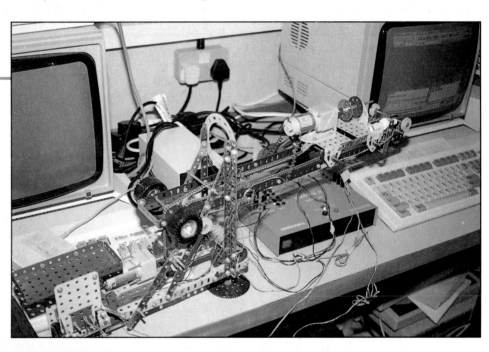

Fig. 8.66 A computer-controlled crane

Fig. 8.67 A computer-controlled conveyor belt system

The Lego model, in Fig. 8.67, is based upon a conveyor-belt system that pupils saw when they visited a food-processing factory. It is designed so that a sensor detects any metal object that might accidentally be mixed in with the food. A computer controls the direction of the sections of the conveyor belt. When a metal object is detected by the sensor, the computer temporarily changes the direction of the next section of the conveyor belt, and the metal object is rejected.

EXTRAS

1. Young children always enjoy pull-along toys. Think of ways of putting some action into a pull-along toy, such as mechanisms that make some part of the toy pop up and down, squeak, flash a light, spin round or wobble about. Make a model of a pull-along toy that includes some of these mechanisms.

151

Structural Systems

Many people think that structures are just large constructions, such as tall buildings, bridges and electricity pylons. These are structures, of course, but so are chairs and drinks cans. Structures are things that provide support.

Most structures are really systems, and are made up of parts called **members**. The structural members work together like a team. In some structures, such as those in an electricity pylons and climbing frames, it is easy to see the individual members. This is because they are **frame structures**. Some other types of structures, like drinks cans and car bodies, do not have a frame, and these are known as **shell structures**. Look at the two types of sledge in Fig. 8.69. One is a wooden frame structure and the other is a shell structure made from a plastic material known as polypropylene.

Fig. 8.68

Fig. 8.69

Structures are made from different materials, depending upon the job the they have to do. Look at the school chair in Fig. 8.70. It consists of a tubular steel frame structure that supports a polypropylene shell structure that in turn supports the sitter. This chair is a structural system that combines both a frame structure and a shell structure. Tubular steel is chosen because it is strong and light. Polypropylene is used because it is tough, easy to mould and easy to keep clean. These materials are chosen because they have the qualities needed for the making and for the everyday use of a school chair.

Fig. 8.70

Structures in nature

Structures are not new. Nature produced the first structures millions of years ago and has been developing them ever since. Egg shells, designed to contain and protect their contents, existed long before drinks cans and car bodies. A spider's web is an extremely strong structure in terms of the weight it will support. You can also think of your body as a complex structural system. Your skeleton provides most of the rigid support for your body, and anchorage for your muscles. It also provides protection and support for delicate and flexible structures, such as your heart and lungs.

In D & T, you will learn to:

recognise that structures have distinctive characteristics including form and stability

design and make structures to take stationary and moving loads

Fig. 8.71

Forces

Structures are designed to withstand forces acting upon them, but sometimes structures collapse or break down. This is called **structural failure**. For example, bridges are designed to carry the weight of traffic or trains crossing them. If a bridge collapses, a terrible accident could occur. Fig. 8.72 shows a picture of the Tay Railway Bridge when it collapsed in 1879.

Fig. 8.72

Chairs are designed for people to sit on, and although they can be made for use by even the heaviest person, they sometimes collapse if a person rocks about, or swings back on them. This is because a chair has been designed to support a **static force**, like that applied by somebody sitting still on it. Chairs are not really designed for **dynamic forces**. Dynamic forces are forces that suddenly change.

Fig. 8.73

Static force   Dynamic force

There are different kinds of forces. Some forces tend to squash structures, like the force that acts on chair legs when somebody sits on a chair. This is called **compression**. Other forces pull – for example a rope when it is used to tow a car. This is called **tension**. Sometimes forces combine to **bend** and **twist** structures (see Fig. 8.74).

Structures often have to be designed to withstand different types of forces, and combinations of forces, that can be both static and dynamic. Think of the changing combinations of forces that an aeroplane has to withstand when it takes off, flies through high winds and thunder storms, and lands.

Fig. 8.74

Bending

Tension

Compression

Twisting

JAM

153

Beams and Bridges

The simplest way of supporting a load across a gap is to use a beam – a horizontal structural member. The earliest types of bridges must have been formed by a tree falling across a river or stream. This accident of nature would have enabled people to cross over the water without getting wet, and also given people the idea of building simple beam bridges.

Bookshelves supported by brackets are simple beam structures. If they are over loaded with heavy books the shelf may bend in the middle. This problem can be solved in several ways. The shelf can be given more support by using another bracket placed near the middle, or the shelf itself can be made thicker or made a different shape.

Fig. 8.75

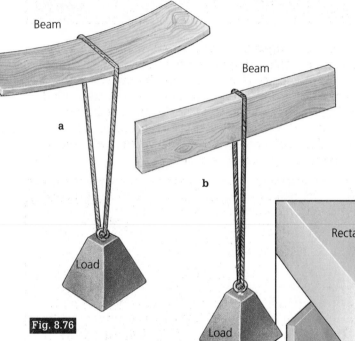
Fig. 8.76

In Fig. 8.76a, a load has been put on a wooden beam. The wood cannot support the forces acting on it and begins to bend. However, if the wood is turned on its edge, the beam is much stronger and resists bending (see Fig. 8.76b). This is because a beam's resistance to bending is greatly increased if its top surface and bottom surface are moved further apart. Some beams even have holes in them and yet they are still very strong. A thicker beam is more rigid than a thin one, but it would be too expensive to always use thick solid beams. They would also be very heavy. Today most beams are made of steel.

When you see beams in use, notice that they are usually used edge-on. Their shapes are more complicated but they are based on the same principle. The different shapes or sections are used to make strong, but light beams. Fig. 8.77 shows some examples of the different types of steel beam used in industry. You can see that they all use the edge-on principle. They are all very strong, but weigh and cost much less than a solid beam. The Britannia Railway Bridge, shown in Fig. 8.78, was designed by Robert Stephenson and built in 1850. The bridge was made from hollow, box-shaped beams, large enough to allow whole trains to pass through the inside.

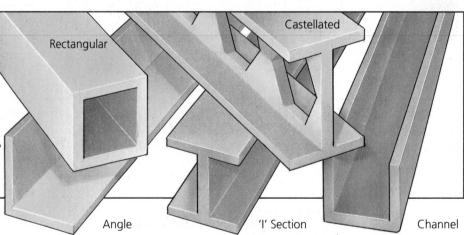
Fig. 8.77 Different types of steel beam used in industry

Fig. 8.78

Arched and suspension bridges

Arched bridges made from stone or brick have been used since Roman times. They are very strong. When blocks (or bricks) are arranged in a semi-circle to form an arch they can withstand a great weight from above. However, the arch must have rigid support to prevent the ends from spreading apart.

Fig. 8.79

Fig. 8.80 A suspension bridge in a mountainous region

Suspension bridges also have a long history. They are called suspension bridges because the bridge is supported from above by cables or chains which are attached to towers. The bridge is therefore suspended (see Fig. 8.80). In parts of the world, such as in the countries to the south of the Himalayas, suspension bridges made of wood and creepers have made remote mountainous regions more accessible.

Cantilevers

Cantilevers are beams that are held and supported at one end only – for example shelf brackets and hanging basket brackets. Sometimes bridges that may look like beam or arched bridges are really two cantilevers that meet in the middle. Many concrete bridges used on motorways are built in this way.

Fig. 8.81

Columns

Columns (and pillars) are vertical beams. They are normally designed to support loads directly on top – for example chair legs and street lamps. Columns are also used to support the roofs of buildings. The Greeks were the first to use columns in this way when they built huge temples such as the Parthenon in Athens (see Fig. 8.82).

Fig. 8.82

EXTRAS

1. Identify as many beams, cantilevers and columns as you can in and around your school. Find out from what material they are made, and how they are made.

2. Collect as many pictures of different types of bridge as you can. What factors do you think have influenced the way each bridge has been made? Is it the availability of materials, the cost of labour, the environment or some other factor?

Stable Structures

A stable structure is one that is safe and will not collapse. There are several ways of making structures more stable. Look at the stool in Fig 8.83a that the elephant is standing on. The force on the stool (caused by the elephant's weight) makes the bottom of the legs move outwards. The stool is unstable. It can be made more stable by adding a bottom rail (see Fig. 8.83b). Many stools and chairs have such a rail. The rail is being stretched in order to keep the stool stable. It is **in tension**. The stability of the stool depends upon the way that the rail is fixed into the legs, and the joints and glue used.

Fig. 8.83

a   b

You may have seen decorators' step ladders that use rope in tension to make them stable and safe (see Fig. 8.84). Rope is very good in tension. The advantage of rope in this situation is that the steps can be folded away after use. Structural members used in tension do not need to be stiff.

Fig. 8.84

Fig. 8.85 Triangulated structures

Triangulation

Instead of a rope, many step ladders today use the top platform to stop the two sides separating. When the platform is fixed in position the step ladder will not open **or** close. This is because the two sides and the platform form a triangle. Even with jointed angles, the shape of a triangle can not be changed or squashed. All other shapes, including squares and rectangles, can be squashed more easily. But by adding one or more additional members and creating a triangle these shapes become stable. This is called **triangulation**. Many structures such as bicycle frames, shelf brackets, house roofs and garden gates are triangulated.

Fig. 8.86

In D&T, you will learn to:
recognise that structures have distinctive characteristics including form and stability
design and make structures to take stationary and moving loads

If you are making a box out of card or wood, and you have joined together the 4 sides but not yet attached the bottom (or top), you will notice that the box is unstable and easily loses its shape. However, when you attach the bottom of the box, it will become stable and keep its shape. This is like adding cross members to form triangles, and then filling in the spaces. It is, in fact, a form of triangulation (see Fig. 8.87).

Fig. 8.87

Fun with Structures

These tasks use everyday materials. You can work on your own or in groups to see who can build the highest, strongest and most stable structure. You could also try them at home with your friends or family, but remember to clean up the mess when you've finished.

Fig. 8.88

Fig. 8.90

1 Each person (or group) will need 10 sheets of newspaper (make sure that the pieces of newspaper are all the same size), 100 mm of sticky tape, and a pair of scissors. Using just these materials, build the tallest self-supporting tower that you can. You may need a room with a high ceiling!

2 Using a single sheet of A4 paper, make a beam bridge that will support 0.5kg over a 200 mm gap. When you have completed your bridge, test it to see how much weight your bridge can support before it collapses.

3 You will need a piece of stiff card 150 mm square and some scissors. Without using any glue or sticky tape, and by only cutting the card into a maximum of 8 separate pieces, build a tower as tall as you can. It is a good idea to practise different ways of slotting or hooking together card before you start constructing your tower.

Fig. 8.89

4 For this task you will need 20 drinking straws (you can cut them into short lengths if you wish), 12 paper clips (you can bend these but you must not cut them), and a hard-boiled egg. Using these materials build a three-legged structure to support the egg as far above the ground as possible. However, the three legs must be standing within a 100 mm diameter circle.

5 Using straws, dress-making pins and one elastic band, build a 'ballista'. (A ballista was an ancient catapult that was used for hurling stones at enemy fortifications.) The ballista should be able to catapult a table-tennis ball 6 metres to land, without bouncing, in a waste-paper basket.

ACKNOWLEDGEMENTS

The publishers would like to thank Anne Bridger, Cathy Burrill and Robert Dransfield for their advice; Denis Prendergast for permission to photograph at Pinner Safeways; and Katy Bradbury for supplying pupils' handwriting.

The publishers would like to thank the following schools for their help with location photography:

Gladesmore Community School, Tottenham (Head of Technology: Cathy Burrill; Pupils: Ganesh Bathmanathan, Lesmi Begum, Nazma Bibi, Faith Connell, Bobby Holmes, Zeyd Hussain, Carl Mehmet, Nomso Okeke, Hassim Sobany, Elif Yeter); Northwood School, Hillingdon (Head of Technology: Jon Lambert; Pupils: Sumaira Chhipa, Elaine Heck, Kashif Khan, Helen Lammin, Scott Marshall, Kay Mulligan, Heidi Roach, Paul Sheppard, Nina Thompson, Melissa Ward, Gavin West, Lisa West) William Farr C of E Comprehensive School, Welton (Head of Technology: Mike Finney).

The publishers would like to thank the following for permission to reproduce photographs and artwork (the name is followed by the figure number, which is followed, where necessary, by (t) top, (b) bottom, (l) left, (r) right):

Apple Computer UK Ltd 2.17, 2.18, 2.23; Argos Distributors Ltd 8.9, 8.46; Belling & Co Ltd 5.52b; The Body Shop 6.49; Graham Bradbury 1.53, 6.20, 8.62; British Gas Plc 5.34; BTTG 1.6, 1.54; Canon UK Ltd 2.27; Colin Chapman 8.66, 8.67; Colour-Rail 8.78; Consumers' Association 6.61; East Midlands Electricity 6.27; Ford Motor Co Ltd 6.15; Frister & Rossmann 1.56; Elida Gibbs 6.25 (t); Sally & Richard Greenhill 4.20, 5.3, 5.6, 5.7, 5.18, 5.19, 5.36, 5.42, 5.53, 8.69 (l); Health Education Authority 6.25 (b); Jeremy Henman 6.14, 6.39; Robert Harding Associates 1.3, 1.9, 1.14, 1.17, 1.32, 4.13, 5.40, 5.46, 6.5a & b, 8.4, 8.64; Michael Holford 1.55; Michael Horsley 6.43, 8.12, 8.13, 8.14, 8.15, 8.18, 8.19, 8.20, 8.24, 8.25, 8.26; Jane Howard PR Ltd 8.11; Hutchison Library 5.38, 5.39, 5.41; IBM 6.34; Ideal Home Exhibition 5.25, 5.27; Jacqui Hurst 1.26, 1.48; Illustrated London News Picture Library 8.72; Peter Jennings 8.55; Jones & Brother 1.24; Littlewoods Organisation Ltd 4.33; Mansell Collection 1.57; Mary Evans Picture Library 6.17; Patrick & Philippa Moyle 1.8, 1.25, 1.31a, 1.41a & b, 4.32, 5.26, 5.51, 6.41, 6.57, 8.50; National Dairy Council 5.55; National Rivers Authority 6.62; Nestlé Co Ltd 6.22; Network p 5 (t); Raleigh Industries Ltd 8.33; Rex Features 1.1, 1.43, 5.21; Ann Ronan Picture Library 1.23; Rowntree Mackintosh Plc 6.26; J Sainsbury Plc 5.56; Science Photo Library 1.58, 1.59, 2.20, 2.22, 4.23 (t,b), 5.32a & b, 6.35, 8.17; Scott Products Ltd 6.23; Shilland & Co Ltd 1.51; Brian Shuel Collections 8.79; Rebecca Sloan 1.49; Stanley Tools 4.53; Stoddard Carpets Ltd 1.12, 1.40, 1.44; Thorntons 6.37, 6.38; Topham Picture Library 1.16, 5.2; Topper International Ltd 4.87; John Walmsley p 5 (b), 3.2; John Watney 8.8; Charlotte & Lucy Watson 8.81; Elizabeth Whiting Associates 1.45, 1.46, 1.47; Zanussi Ltd 5.52a; Zefa p 5 (l), 1.7, 1.10, 1.11, 1.15, 1.18, 1.19, 1.20, 1.22, 1.42, 4.27, 5.5, 5.21, 5.37, 7.2, 7.3, 7.9, 7.12, 7.14, 7.15, 7.16, 8.1, 8.7, 8.21a & b, 8.69 (r), 8.71, 8.80, 8.82.

INDEX